It was Corn-Flower who, months later, sighted a dust cloud rolling along the desert. *See page 95.*

THE BOOK OF
INDIANS

by

Holling C. Holling

ILLUSTRATED BY

H. C. and Lucille Holling

NEW YORK
THE PLATT & MUNK CO. Inc.
PUBLISHERS

TO FRAN BLACK

You were too young to remember the wind in the sand, the tide ebbing, and one lone Indian dipping his net in the surf. But you are growing up. And, when you are old enough to read this book for yourself, remember this about the old-time Indians . . . . They were men. They were honest. They faced life unafraid . . . .

Be a good Indian.

CONTENTS

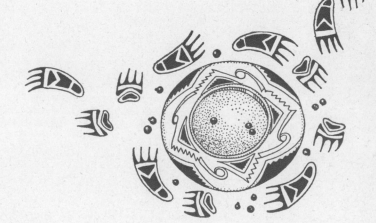

LIST OF COLORED ILLUSTRATIONS

FOREWORD

As a boy, I wanted to know all about Indians. How did they really live? Did they always have horses? Did they always wear war-bonnets? How did they make those arrowpoints that Grandfather found in the fields? There were thousands of questions in my mind, and very few answers in the books I had.

In later years I began to look for the answers in many places. I am still asking questions. In all parts of the country scientists are digging in the earth, writing about what they have found, and the things they find and the books they write are being stored in museums and libraries. Mrs. Holling and I have visited these museums and libraries and have talked with the scientists themselves. Besides that we have lived with Indians. In the northern forests we paddled their birch-bark canoes, and slept in their wickiups. We rode our horses beside theirs across the great plains and camped in their teepees in the mountains. In the desert they made us feel at home in their pueblos. We have fished with them in the surf of the Pacific Ocean. This book is the result of some of that hunting, riding, camping and research.

No writer can tell all about the North American Indians in one book, and no artist can draw all the pictures there are to draw. The tribes of Indians are so many that if we tried to tell about them as *tribes* everyone would be hopelessly lost. Instead, we take the Indians as a whole and divide them into different *types* of Indians living in different *kinds* of country. This is explained in the first chapter. In the rest of the book there are four chapters about the home life of Indian children and eight chapters relating their adventures.

Here are a few things to keep in mind while reading this book: In most tribes the Indian child did not take a father's clan as we take the name of a father, but was classed as the mother's child. A father remained adviser to his son or daughter, but generally he did not have a great deal to do with their daily lives. The mother's brother became friend, teacher, and all-around "big brother."

Love of battle was characteristic of most Indians. To them the battle ground proved manhood and courage.

Their code of honor was rigid, though often misunderstood by us.

Horses were not known to the Indians until the Spaniards came to America.

Indians do not show much humor among whites. However, there is scarcely a more fun-loving, joke-enjoying people than they are among themselves.

H. C. HOLLING.

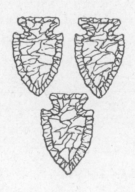

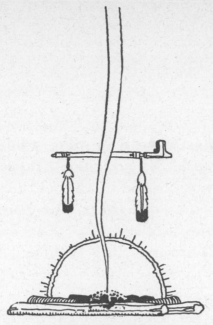

CHAPTER I

SOMETHING ABOUT INDIANS

Nobody knows how long Indians have lived on this Continent. Thousands of years ago they were here. It is thought that they came from Asia long ago, crossing over from Siberia to Alaska. In America they found a good land, with mountains and plains, lakes and rivers, forests and deserts. The water held fish, the air was alive with birds, and game was everywhere. At first these people moved about over the country, until they found the place that suited them. Then they settled down to build homes and raise families. This went on for thousands of years, although the rest of the world knew nothing about them.

We call these people "Indians," but the name was given them through a mistake. Traders from Europe wanted the spices, the gold and the jewels of India; but if they went by land, great mountains and deserts had to be crossed, and the way by sea was rough and dangerous. Christopher Columbus thought he could sail to India by a shorter way, so he sailed westward from Spain and found America. He thought that it was India which he had reached, and when the natives with red-brown skins paddled to meet him in their canoes, he took them to be natives of that country. So he called them "Indians," and we still use that word today.

[13]

America is made up of many different kinds of country. Some parts are covered with heavy forests. Other parts are open, rolling plains. Still others have hot, dry deserts. There are sections where great mountains tower to the sky, and others where the sea dashes against the coasts. In the days before Columbus, Indians lived in all these different kinds of country. They were split up into tribes, but all the tribes in one kind of country lived in about the same way.

For instance, in the Forest Country, between the Mississippi River and the East Coast, there are a great many rivers and lakes. The Indians of this section traveled about in canoes. In the north, where birch trees grew, they made their canoes of birch-bark. In the south, they used "dugouts," made by hollowing out a tree trunk. They built houses of poles covered with the bark of trees. They hunted, fished, and planted small gardens for food. They were the People of the Forests, and the decorations they painted on their deer-skins or wove into their baskets or sewed onto their clothing with bright porcupine quills came from the forests. They were designs of leaves, vines and flowers.

West of the Forest People, between the Mississippi River and the Rocky Mountains, lived the People of the Plains and Mountains. They had no deep woods. They knew only open prairies sweeping in every

direction. These people built their houses of driftwood from the river bottoms, covered with grass from the plains and roofed with earth. When the great winds blew across the prairies, or blizzards howled in the wintertime, their warm fires kept them comfortable in these houses.

Sometimes they went on long hunts after the buffalo. Then they used small, pointed tents, made of skins, which were light enough to be dragged by dogs. After the white men came, bringing horses, the Plains Indians made larger tents and left the earth-covered houses. Then they wandered all over the open plains, and far into the Rocky Mountains. Their main food was buffalo meat. They knew nothing but great stretches of flat country, hot sun, round moon, bright stars, and jagged mountains; so in the designs they painted, wove or embroidered, were straight lines and triangles, circles and squares.

At the south end of the Rocky Mountains, in Arizona and New Mexico, lived the People of the Desert. Water was scarce here, so the villages were always built near water. At first these people lived in caves in the canyon walls, but later they made great apartment buildings in huge, steep pyramids, called pueblos. The houses were made of the rocks found everywhere, plastered with the earth itself, which made a solid, firm mud. One pueblo housed an entire city.

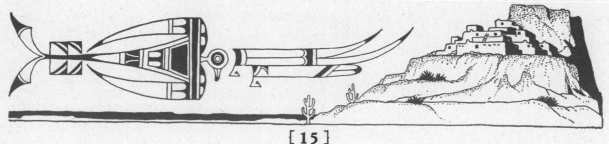

The Desert Indians were not wanderers, as the Plains Indians were. They stayed at home and tended their gardens. They were the farmers of early America, and grew the best corn, beans, squash and peppers in the country. There was brilliant color in the rocks and mountains among which they lived, and the designs on their pottery and in their weaving were copied from the things they knew best. Some were rock designs. Some were clouds. Some were desert animals, birds and reptiles. And most of them were painted as good luck symbols to bring rain and good crops.

In the northwest, from Washington north along the Canadian coast to Alaska, lived the People of the Sea. They lived where great cedar trees grew. Because they had a certain kind of stone which made fine, sharp tools, they delighted in working with wood. The cedar trees could be split easily, so they built houses of cedar planks. Their canoes were cedar logs, hollowed out, and made large enough to go to sea. These people hunted land animals sometimes, but they lived principally on fish and whale meat and seal. They were fishing people, and the designs they carved were suggested by the animals and fish known along their coasts. They carved and painted their histories on great poles which they set before their houses. We now call them "totem poles."

There are many more divisions of Indians in America, but these four are the most important. These are the people we tell about in this book. To do so, we tell about a little boy and a little girl from each of these sections of country. First we tell how they lived, and then we go with them on their adventures.

[16]

CHAPTER II

PEOPLE OF THE FORESTS AND LAKES

Otter-Tail and his girl cousin, Flying-Squirrel, were little Indians of the Forests. From babyhood they had learned that the woods and lakes were their best friends. Food, clothing, shelter, tools—these things all came from the forest.

Their village was in a meadow on the shore of a beautiful lake. Rounded bark houses were built around an open space where great dances were sometimes held. Back of the houses were gardens, and close behind these were maple, basswood, birch, pine and fir trees like a crowd of warriors always on guard. Birch-bark canoes were lined up on the sandy beach. At the tops of poles, platforms holding deer hides and drying meat, leaned this way and that, like huge bird nests on stilts. The air of the village was filled with the smoke of many fires.

One day Wolverine, Otter-Tail's father, decided to build a new house near the center of the village. He selected a place where the ground was flat and even, and with a stick he marked an oval about twenty feet long and twelve feet wide. Along this line Wolverine dug holes two feet apart, and in them set smooth, green saplings. He bent the tops over to make arches, and bound them together with withes.

Otter-Tail made these withes. He cut basswood saplings three inches thick, and peeled them. The gray, outer bark came away easily, leaving a long sheet of slippery white bark beneath. This was as limber as rubber, and from it the Indians stripped any kind of tying material—thongs the thickness of a shoe-lace, larger cords for twisting into ropes, or fine string for fish lines or nets.

When the house frame was finished, with poles going around it as well as over the top, it looked like a huge bird cage. Then Wolverine made the walls of cedar bark sheets, flattened out to form large shingles. He tied them to the pole frame with basswood ropes. In forests farther south, shingles of elm or oak bark were used, or sometimes rush mats tightly woven covered a whole house. But this village was in the Great Lakes region, and because it was so easy to get, birch bark made the roof of Otter-Tail's new home. His mother, helped by Flying-Squirrel, had sewn squares of the bark end to end until they had several strips about twenty feet long, like rolls of carpeting.

Wolverine now laid these strips, called "apakwas," over the rounded frame, in overlapping layers, and tied them down with basswood ropes so that the wind could not rip off the roof. A square hole in the center of the roof was the only chimney. In a doorway at one end of the house Wolverine made a half-gate of poles, to keep the dogs out, and the house was finished.

Such forest dwellings were called "wickiups." A whole village of them looked very much like a scattering of huge loaves of bread. When the white men came, later on, they heard the word "wig-was-i-ga-mig," meaning "bark house." This they shortened to "wig-was" and finally to "wig-wam," and called every kind of Indian dwelling—hut—or teepee—by that name. However, for these rounded houses the word "wickiup" is best.

The fireplace was a square pen of logs or stones on the ground beneath the smoke hole. A platform of smooth poles two feet high

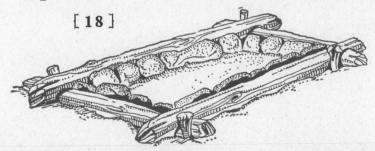

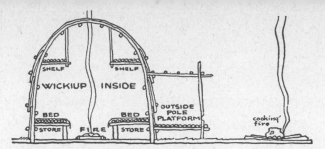

ran all around the wickiup. On this platform Wolverine's family worked or slept. For beds they used rush mats or fir boughs. Deer skins or bear robes made the lower blankets, while the top ones were of beaver or fox skins sewn together. The favorite warm robe of the Forest Indian was made of rabbit skins woven into fuzzy blankets.

Otter-Tail's people lived outdoors more than indoors, except in cold or rainy weather, but they used the wickiup for storing their food and other belongings, either against the roof on shelves made of poles, or under the beds.

On the outside of the wickiup, near the door, another platform built against the wall was shaded by a bark or bough awning. Here women and girls spent most of their time, squatting with feet tucked under—sewing, tanning skins, preparing food. Flying-Squirrel's family and Otter-Tail's worked together most of the time, and here was the place for talking over the village gossip. The family dogs, of which there were many, snoozed under this platform. There was always a scrap of meat to be hoped for, because the cooking fire was just a few feet away and a clay pot was forever simmering on the red coals.

Flying-Squirrel kept the earth about the fire spotlessly clean. She shoveled the ashes into bark boxes for household uses. Then she swept the hearth with a grass broom, and sprinkled it several times a day with gourds of water. After such care the ground became as level and solid as a cement sidewalk.

Otter-Tail dressed like his father. In summer, about the camp, they wore only a loin cloth or breech cloth of soft buckskin. When they traveled they wore moccasins. Hair was a bother in brush and brambles, so Forest Indians shaved their heads with flint knives, leaving only a tuft of hair on top, which was neatly braided. This was the "scalp-lock."

Wolverine and Otter-Tail had scalp ornaments for special occasions. These were "roaches," or huge brushes of brilliantly dyed deer hair, fitted over the scalp lock. In these roaches flopped eagle

[19]

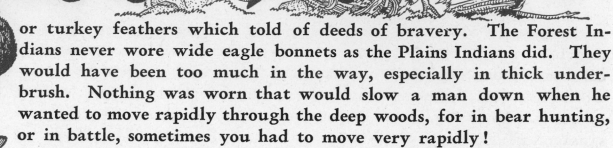

or turkey feathers which told of deeds of bravery. The Forest Indians never wore wide eagle bonnets as the Plains Indians did. They would have been too much in the way, especially in thick underbrush. Nothing was worn that would slow a man down when he wanted to move rapidly through the deep woods, for in bear hunting, or in battle, sometimes you had to move very rapidly!

At the waist was the most important part of the Forest Indian's costume. This was his belt. From it dangled a decorated sheath with its precious knife—a flint blade set into a carved wood handle. The belt held the war-club, too. Knives were used mostly for skinning animals taken in hunting and for cutting meat. They were no use for stabbing black bears or other large beasts. One glancing blow on a rib bone and the blade broke. But the club was a different matter. Some clubs were made entirely of wood, with a polished ball head. Others had a rounded stone head bound with rawhide to the wooden handle. The true "tomahawk" was a smooth, polished axe-head or "celt" of stone driven into a hole in the wooden grip. Either a club or a tomahawk would stop a bear, panther or man, if handled correctly, but Wolverine and Otter-Tail preferred the tomahawk. Wolverine could throw his so cleverly that it would split a twig at twenty paces—and he was teaching his son to do the same.

Otter-Tail's belt held his only pockets. From it dangled a buckskin pouch with porcupine quill designs all over it. What was inside? There are many things a boy can pick up in the woods and use, and this pouch was full of such things as pieces of flint for new knives, bits of sinew for sewing, a bone awl and bone fish hooks. So whether his scalp-lock was neatly braided or not, Otter-Tail was never without his belt and all that went with it. You never could tell what might come along the trail!

[20]

In winter, when days were bitter cold and the sun slept, the men and boys put on warm clothing. Then Otter-Tail wore moccasins of moose hide, puckered on top, and lined with rabbit fur. Instead of trousers he wore long leggings with fringe and designs worked in quills. He pulled them on one leg, then the other, like separate sausage casings, and tied them to his belt at the hips. These kept his legs warm for wading in snow drifts. Above the belt his skin was tough, and he wore no shirt; but when it was really cold he pulled long fur muffs over each arm, full length, much as he put on his leggings, and fastened them by tying straps across his back and chest. Usually in the winter he walked about camp with a soft robe of beaver skins thrown over his shoulder and belted at the waist. Overcoats? Stockings? Underwear? He had never heard of such things, and only in the far north did the Indians wear peaked fur caps, or "parkas" over their heads.

Hanging about camp, in summer, was tiresome. It was all right for girls and women, who had to sew and weave, but a boy's place was in the woods. Adventure and action and a world of learning were to be found in the forests.

Otter-Tail never tired of studying the habits of the woodland creatures. Thousands of birds swarmed in the swamps and along the lakes—ducks, geese, herons, cranes and snipe. The open meadows among the trees, where grass grew and berry bushes scrambled over logs—that was the place for quail, grouse and partridge, and at certain times of the year the skies were darkened by clouds of wild pigeons. When he was very young, Otter-Tail could mimic the gobble of wild turkeys.

Beavers left tree stumps along every stream as they forever repaired their dams and built their wickiups of poles and mud. Muskrats swam everywhere, diving for lily roots for winter storage. Wolverines, skunks, weasels and minks prowled the underbrush near streams. And that master fisherman, the otter, with his webbed feet,

[21]

WOLVERINE

swam in the lakes or played "follow the leader" down his mud slides into the river.

Wolverine taught Otter-Tail how to stalk game and how to hunt and trap smaller animals and birds. Arrows were useful sometimes. At other times a deftly set snare, twisted from human hair or sinew, caught more game than could be brought down by the arrows of several hunters working together. With his father the boy roamed the game trails and set deadfalls of heavy logs for fox, wolf, lynx or bear, baited with meat smeared with fish oil. Of course the finest hunting was a man's job—the shooting of deer, elk or moose—and Otter-Tail had been promised a real hunt with Wolverine and his uncle Moose-Heart, Flying-Squirrel's father.

Otter-Tail's hunting bow had been made by his grandfather. It was of tough hickory, and had a graceful curve when strung with the sinew cord. His best arrow shafts were willow shoots peeled, straightened and seasoned over the fire and smoothed with sandstone. Wolverine used arrow points of flint, flaked on the palm of his hand with a piece of deer antler. But a boy misses many shots in practice, so Otter-Tail's points were of bone and antler ground sharp. They were set into the split end of the shaft and bound snug with wet sinew which hardened as it dried. Goose and turkey feathers at the ends made the arrows fly straight to their mark. For ordinary work Otter-Tail used unfeathered arrows with blunt wood heads, because it was easy to make new ones to replace any that he lost. Even with these clumsy arrows, he got many a squirrel and partridge.

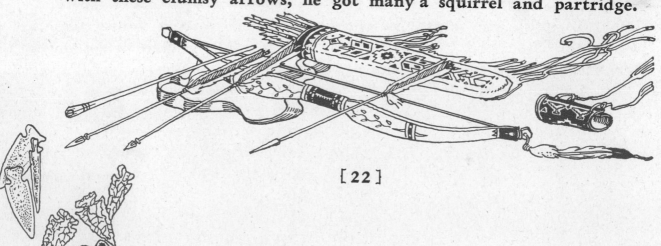

Hunting, with Indians, was not merely a sport; it was a necessity. They used almost all of each animal for some purpose, and killed only what they needed. They never slaughtered for the sake of seeing animals die. Thus the woods were always full of game, and the streams and lakes never ran out of fish. Before killing, the Forest Indians usually asked permission of the animal's spirit, telling it that its body was needed for the welfare of the people. And after skinning an animal, the hunter tied the tail or a tuft of hair to a twig, as a thank offering to the departed spirit.

Flying-Squirrel was one of the hardest workers among the girls. When she saw something to be done she did it without being told. Always the first one up in the morning, she blew the coals out of their ashes and made the breakfast fire. Her baby brother was her doll. While the others dressed she made a new nest of fresh, dried moss in his papoose cradle, tied him snugly in and hung him up on the wickiup wall out of the way.

Babies tied to a cradle-board grew up with straight backs and straight legs. Because their arms were tied down too, with soft buckskin wrappings, they never worked their hands all over their faces, and thumb sucking was unknown. Babies brought up in the Indian manner were never fretful and nervous, and seldom cried.

Flying-Squirrel took a cold plunge in the lake every morning. Then she brushed her hair with a comb and brush made from a porcupine's tail. Her hair was twisted into a "club" at the back and wrapped with bright buckskin. Her dresses were simple, made of buckskin, with arm muffs like those Otter-Tail wore in winter, tied across the chest and back with soft straps. All the other girls and the women wore the same sort of clothing.

[23]

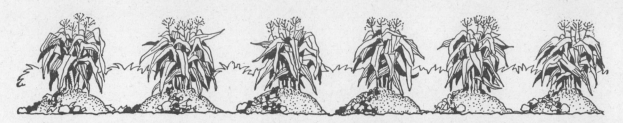

After bringing buckets of fresh water, Flying-Squirrel aired the bedding by spreading it on bushes and poles. If she spied a hole in the roof of the house she patched it with new bark. Then she went to the garden to weed before the sun was really above the trees.

That garden was cleverly made. Indians had no plows. They didn't need them. They cleared the underbrush away from a space and carried in rich earth, which they piled in hills about two feet high. The hills were made in rows and the Indians walked along the rows planting corn in the top of each hill. From this method used by Indians we get the term "a hill of corn." On the south side of each hill they planted squash and pumpkin seeds. The vines grew around the hill, the vegetables lying on the ground below when ripe. Weeding this garden was very easy. Flying-Squirrel did not need to stoop far over, because she weeded only the hill itself. The rest of the patch could grow up to weeds, it did not matter.

What did these people of the forest eat? They had squashes and pumpkins, stewed or baked. Corn was boiled green or roasted in the husk, or dried and stored. By boiling dried corn with wood ashes, they made hominy, and by pounding it in a log mortar, they made corn meal for bread, cakes and mush. From the lakes came wild rice, harvested in canoes. Roots of bulrush and yellow water lily tasted like potatoes. In the spring came all sorts of greens, including fern tips, dandelions and milkweed shoots. They had raspberries, blueberries and other wild fruits; and the trees in the fall yielded bushels of nuts of every kind. The Indians of the Forest did not use salt, so they were not bothered by mosquitoes. Salt, they said, caused an odor in perspiration which attracted many insects. Instead they seasoned some meats and their mush with maple sugar, of which they had plenty. With these foods, and many varieties of meat and fish, the people of the Forests lived well.

Even with these clumsy arrows the boy brought down many a squirrel and partridge. *See page 22.*

Flying-Squirrel liked to work on the pole platform beside her grandmother, Mink-Woman. Granny knew everything. She knew why the blackbird has a red wing and where the wind came from. She predicted when it would rain and knew what kind of roots to chew for stomach ache. She taught Flying-Squirrel how to tie knots for fish nets; and, when it came to weaving, her old brown fingers were faster than a spider's legs. She made fine twine from nettle fibre, and from this wove carrying bags with colored vine designs. She wove baskets from grass, from roots, from splints. She also wove the best rush mats in the village, and her clay cooking pots were sought after by all the other women. Tanning was easy for her. She could make a whole birch-bark canoe all by herself, and she taught her granddaughter how to paddle, swim and carry a canoe at a portage.

Thus Otter-Tail and Flying-Squirrel lived and worked in this great land of Forests and Lakes.

CHAPTER III

OTTER-TAIL GOES HUNTING

It was the moon of falling leaves, and Otter-Tail had been promised a hunting trip with his father Wolverine and his uncle Moose-Heart.

"Remember, you must be ready by dawn, or we'll leave you behind," said Uncle Moose-Heart, who loved to tease.

Otter-Tail had no intention of being left behind. He collected his best bone-tipped arrows and all his gear in the evening, and when the men came at dawn the next morning, there he stood on the landing log all ready to start.

"Well, spring-my-rabbit snares!" exclaimed Moose-Heart. "Been standing here like a carved ladle-handle all night? You must want to go hunting!"

"Huh! Can't a man sleep under a canoe without everybody being surprised?" asked Otter-Tail, trying to speak in a matter-of-fact way, as he began to help with the loading of the canoe.

"A man, he calls himself! Listen, Wolverine; your son, who has seen eight summers, calls himself a man! Split-my-moccasins! If he catches anything bigger than a rabbit this trip, the village won't hold him! Get going, chipmunk, and catch this bundle. And don't get it wet!"

Wolverine smiled but did not say anything. Otter-Tail and his uncle were always joking this way with each other.

When the last bundle had been stored, they pushed away from the log. Soon the sky grew red in the east, and the sun scattered the Frost Warriors so that they drifted like smoke over the forest. And what a forest it was! On fire with scarlet and gold and orange,

bathed in browns and dull greens. Plop-swish went the paddles, and quickly they were on their way.

Toward the upper end of the lake Moose-Heart stopped paddling.

"Skin-me-for-a-badger," he exclaimed. "We've forgotten our breakfast! Wolverine—what do you bet I get a muskellunge before we reach the portage?"

"I think," said Wolverine, his eyes twinkling, "you're a very good man if you can get one at this end of the lake. In fact, I'll bet you my moccasins with the red hill designs in quillwork, that you can't. If I win, I want the run-around pipe stem you carved last year."

"Oh! So he wants my stem-that-turns-like smoke, Otter-Tail! Well, he won't get it, for I have the best trolling line in the north, and the best luck!" And with that he let out a bone hook with polished bone spinner, decorated with hairs from a deer's tail. The basswood line went out and out.

"Whee!" cried Otter-Tail, as a jerk on the line almost upset the canoe. "That fish must be hungry this morning, for he's got it already!"

"Has he!" exclaimed Moose-Heart. "And now, Wolverine, who wins the bet?"

"One thing to hook a fish, another thing to land him," said Wolverine.

The big fish had headed out toward the open lake and was towing the light canoe as though it had been a leaf. The line was strong, however, and it held. At length Moose-Heart began hauling in, little by little, hand over hand.

"Look, Uncle Moose-Heart, he's coming up! There's his back fin! You can spear him from here," cried Otter-Tail, handing a many-pointed spear to his uncle. The muskellunge wasn't tired out by any means. He had just come to the surface to decide what to do next; but he decided too late, for the spear leaped out and landed close

[27]

behind that back fin. The water swirled; Otter-Tail helped pull on the line; and, after a tussle, a fine muskellunge lay in the canoe.

"Who's a gopher now?" crowed Moose-Heart, but Wolverine only smiled.

"Fool's luck," he said. "Besides, I didn't want those moccasins any more. And remember—he who catches a fish, scales him!"

At the portage they had a meal of thick, fresh "musky" steaks broiled on peeled sticks. Then the carry began. Wolverine and Otter-Tail took the bundles, while Moose-Heart turned the canoe over and balanced it on his head, and all went single file up the trail to the next lake.

The canoes used by Otter-Tail's tribe were perfect boats for this kind of wilderness travel. Light cedar made the ribs and planking, and over all was a tight shell of birch bark, sewn with split spruce roots and calked with tar made from pine pitch and soot. If a canoe was smashed in the rapids, there were always cedar trees, birches and other necessary material at hand to patch and mend it. It was light for portage so that when one lake ended, it could be picked up and carried to the next. Or when a traveler could not go up a rapids, he got out and carried it around the bad place. In a day's travel he might make many such carries, but it was all in the day's work.

On the next lake the two men and Otter-Tail paddled until dusk. Then they camped on a small island. That evening they were to go "jack-lighting" for deer, so Wolverine rigged up the equipment.

He fixed two poles to the gunwales so that they stuck out in front of the canoe, like tusks. At the end, between them, he swung a birch bark box filled with sand. Meanwhile Otter-Tail was gathering a good pile of pine-knots, full of pitch and resin, which he stored in the bow of the canoe. One of these would burn for a long time.

Before they started, Otter-Tail lighted one of the pine knots at the campfire. Then he put out the campfire and set the lighted torch in the sand box. It was dark by this time and they pushed off.

Otter-Tail was fire tender. His blazing knot flared, but the sand kept it from burning the box or the canoe. Between the box and the bow of the canoe was a large shield of bark. The white side was toward the blazing pine knot so that it reflected the light out in front, like the headlight on an automobile, and no glare got into the eyes of the hunters.

All animals, especially deer and moose, are attracted by fire. They are frightened by it, and will not come too close, but they want to find out what it is that glows like the sun in the darkness. So the men paddled the craft close along the reedy shores, where the deer came to drink in the evening.

Otter-Tail, crouching behind the shield, kept putting out a newly lighted knot as fast as one burned out. He could see the forest by this searchlight. The rushes looked like green threads and the dead trees out over the water like gnarled giants. Birch trunks gleamed white. A red maple branch seemed on fire with the light.

And then, in a patch of black shadow, two golden spots glowed close together. They were the eyes of a deer, reflecting the light from the torch. Moose-Heart stood up quietly, balancing himself, while Wolverine kept the canoe steady with his paddle. Otter-Tail

[29]

heard the twang of a bowstring behind him and saw one flash as the arrow sped through the light. Then the two spots of fire went out. There was a splashing in the water, a crash in the brush, and a heavy thud.

"Got him," said Moose-Heart, and they paddled quickly to the spot. There was a swirl of gray mud where the animal had been standing in the lake, and the rushes were bent over. Lighted by the torch, Moose-Heart stepped out on a stone and went into the underbrush. There was a moment of silence, then a swishing of branches, and Moose-Heart stood again on the shore, a buck deer on his broad shoulders.

Otter-Tail was trembling with excitement. This was the first "jack-lighting" he had seen done. What a beautiful deer! Its coat glowed red-brown in the light. From its left side, just behind the shoulder, the feathered end of the arrow stood out.

"You see, Otter-Tail," Uncle Moose-Heart said, as Wolverine helped him roll the buck into the canoe, careful not to let his antlers puncture the bark shell, "a man can shoot a bow as well at night as in the daylight. You will find, after you practice enough, that shooting will become as easy as pointing your finger. You don't have to worry about seeing your bow and arrow—just seeing what you shoot at is the thing. I saw those two eyes. I knew they were head-on, so I waited a second until your father turned the canoe sideways, to the left. That made the deer turn enough to one side so I could gauge the distance from his eyes to his shoulder. When I saw a fleck of red between the rushes, I let him have it. And now, if you aren't all tired out, we might be able to get one more along the bottom end of the lake—the canoe will hold it. What do you say?"

Wolverine changed places with Moose-Heart, and soon they found two spots of light again in the darkness, but Wolverine could not get a proper shot at the side of the deer.

Otter-Tail heard a soft rustle and looked around. There was

[30]

just enough light for him to see that his father had put down his
bow and was fumbling at his belt. In a moment up came the good
old stone-headed tomahawk in his hand. There was a lunge that
made the canoe shudder from end to end. Otter-Tail heard a heavy
sound and one loud splash, and the water ringed about the canoe in
little waves. Then the light came to rest on the water again, and the
red back of another deer showed just above the surface. When the
men had lifted up the head, there lay the tomahawk with its stone
blade buried in the deer's skull, exactly between the eyes.

"Well, my son," said Wolverine solemnly, though his eyes danced,
"you see that not only an arrow can be aimed well at night."

Back on the island the men hung the animals on a pole between
trees, and swiftly skinned and dressed them. While his father and
uncle were busy with the deer, Otter-Tail kept a bright fire burning.

"And now, what will you have for supper?" asked Uncle Moose-
Heart, "venison tenderloin or broiled tongue?"

What a night that was for Otter-Tail! As the steaks sputtered
on the red coals, far off across the lake a wolf howled mournfully.

"You can see now why we camped on a small island," said Wolverine. "There aren't any animals on this pile of rocks to come
prowling around the meat tonight."

After they had finished their supper, the three Indians sat around
the fire listening to the voices of the night. Out over the lake the
doleful cry of a loon wailed. Then a huge moon swung up. As
Otter-Tail watched, he saw a flock of geese cut the moon in two.

Soon his eyelids began to grow heavy. He was tired out from all
the excitement, and it was growing very cold. There would be a
heavy frost again. He was glad when his father spread one of the
deer hides down on the fir boughs he had collected for a bed.

[31]

In the morning he slept late. The first thing he saw when he had awakened, was a low frame of poles with a smoky fire burning under it and hundreds of strips of meat hanging from the poles. The deer meat was being "jerked." Indians, especially in drying meat, took it off layer by layer in thin, long strips. When game was shot near camp the fresh meat was generally carried in; but this meat was to go into storage for the winter, so it was being dried. After it was thoroughly dried Wolverine and Moose-Heart showed Otter-Tail how to pack it tightly in bark containers, so they could carry it with them on the trip.

Several days passed. Moose-Heart got another deer, and Wolverine shot a bear, but Otter-Tail had shot only squirrels and rabbits.

"Shucks!" he said. "I can do that any day, on the edge of the village. I want to shoot something real!" But the men were busy, and time was precious, and it was a week before he had any sort of a chance at all.

Both men had shot at a moose at the edge of a swamp and wounded him with arrows. Moose-Heart held the canoe while Wol-

verine trailed the animal into a bog. Otter-Tail was tired of squatting in the canoe, so he took his best arrows and went ashore. He wandered up a long slope and down the other side without seeing anything interesting. To Otter-Tail the trip was a complete failure. How could he face his chums back home without something in the big-game line, to show for all this time on a hunt?

Then, looking down, he saw that the swamp into which the moose had run curved around behind the hill he had just walked over. Down there in the marshy growth something was happening. The willows swayed, and Otter-Tail heard a strange noise. Cautiously he crept down to the edge of the swamp and out onto a small island of firm ground. Then his eyes bulged, for he saw the moose, with head down and the great scoop horns on each side of something which wiggled and turned in the blueberry bushes. This something had human legs and moccasins on the feet. The moose was trying to kill his father!

Otter-Tail scrambled over the bogs as fast as his feet would carry him. There was that great brown beast with gray legs towering above the willows. Never had anything looked so huge to Otter-Tail. He was frightened, but then he saw the eyes of his father peering at him in an odd way. Wolverine had his hands on the huge antlers. He was hanging on, and his body lay between them. The great head of the bull came up and went down, and Wolverine's body came up and went down with it, like a piece of wet rawhide flapping in the wind. Then Otter-Tail went into action.

His hands had been shaking before, but now they were as firm as though he were going after a chipmunk. He carefully picked the very best bone-headed arrow from his woodchuck quiver. Right up toward that moose he went, until he could see the great ribs heaving. He notched his arrow and pulled with all the strength in his arms, and Grandfather's bow went back and back. Then, plock! And the arrow buried itself halfway up the shaft.

[33]

The beast snorted and lunged, and Wolverine's body went spinning away to land in a mud hole. But Otter-Tail wasn't finished yet. He had another arrow on the string, and before the bull moose could pull his front feet out of the muck, the boy had driven another shaft into that brown side. The beast made one lunge and fell on its nose, then rolled over dead.

Wolverine came running up. He was scratched and bleeding from many cuts, but he was not seriously hurt. He hugged his son to his muddy body so that the boy's mouth was full of mud. The lad had not known whether to laugh or cry, but the mud in his mouth kept him from doing either. He went down to a pool to wash his face, and when he returned Wolverine was sitting on the dead moose, getting his breath.

That moose was a huge one, with heavy antlers. The first two arrows shot by the men had merely enraged him, and he had hid in a windfall of tangled brush. When Wolverine had come around the side of it, and slipped on a bog, the moose had charged the man furiously. Had it not been for Otter-Tail, his father might never have returned from this hunting trip.

When the two of them had got back to Moose-Heart and he had heard the tale, he looked at Otter-Tail oddly. All he said was, "Scalp me with a duck's foot!" But that from Moose-Heart was quite a compliment.

So the hunt ended happily, and when they reached camp with dried meat enough to feed everybody for many weeks, Wolverine himself set the moose antlers up on the wickiup roof, so that all might see that Otter-Tail was a real hunter.

CHAPTER IV

FLYING-SQUIRREL GATHERS BULRUSHES

Flying-Squirrel was proud of her cousin, Otter-Tail, the brave hunter who had killed a moose. While they husked corn, the girls talked it all over time and again. But that did not slow up the corn-husking. Swish, swosh—two movements, and the husk came off the yellow ear. Plop, and the ear went into the basket. What a glorious time it was! Trees all yellow and red, platforms golden with heaped ears, orange and brown pumpkins and squashes being cut into long corkscrews for drying.

When the first frosts had tumbled the nuts from the trees, the children raced squirrels for them. Walnuts and butternuts were hulled, and the hulls saved for dyeing quills. Beechnuts, hazelnuts, hickory nuts—baskets bulged with them.

Men and boys were setting snares and deadfalls these days. Up little marshy creeks they paddled, finding beaver ponds and otter slides. Many piles of soft pelts came home in the canoes.

Then Winter Spirits breathed cold blasts on the lakes and changed them to ice, so that the canoes were of no use and must be stored. The women and girls helped in this work. The bark boats were lined up side by side on a stretch of sandy beach high above the lake and were completely covered with sand, so that nothing could be seen but a series of long mounds.

"You see," said Grandmother Mink-Woman to Flying-Squirrel, "now the wood and bark of the canoes will not dry out and crack. When spring comes, and we take them out of their dens again, they will be like new."

Moose-Heart, Otter-Tail and Wolverine were making new snow-shoes and mending old ones. While Wolverine bent the spruce and cedar frames, Otter-Tail cut thongs for the webbing. From a disc of dried deerhide as big as a dishpan he pared a continuous string, around and around. It seemed endless, it was so long. Then Moose-Heart soaked it until it was just right, and wove the intricate mesh patterns for walking on soft snow.

On clear pond or lake ice, the children played their old, old ice game. It was the shinney or hockey still played today. Sticks were carefully curved, and carved in gay patterns. And that block of wood, the puck, went spinning from goal to goal. The Indian children had no skates, only moccasins, but the game was played swiftly with a grand rumpus of flying sticks, arms and legs. And nobody enjoyed it more than the dogs, who were always tangled up with everything.

Then came Winter in earnest.

The wickiup village was a huddle of snow-covered mounds, each mound smoking in the middle. Trails led from door to door, and piles of dead wood were everywhere. The women and girls had gathered it from the lower tree trunks—dry, firm limbs, still called "squaw wood" in some sections. Men were continually clumping in on their snowshoes from the forest, bringing rabbits and partridges from their snares, foxes, wolverines and fishers from their deadfalls.

Flying-Squirrel and Grandmother Mink-Woman dried the rabbit skins on frames. When the drying had been completed, the girl cut the skins into strips, sewed them end to end, and twisted the long strip into a cord. The fur sprayed out all around, making a thick fuzzy rope. From these ropes Grandmother Mink-Woman wove warm, soft blankets.

Now was the time for porcupine quill embroidery. Moccasins, leggings, knife sheaths and anything that needed good colorful decoration were brought out. When the quills had been plucked from porcupine skins, they had been chalk white with sharp black tips at one end; but they had been dyed throughout the year and stored in skin envelopes, color by color. Grandmother Mink-Woman had taught Flying-Squirrel how to prepare the dyes. Goldenrod and yellow-root made yellow; walnut hulls made brown; butternut hulls made black. Blood-root and sumac gave shades of orange and red, and blueberries made a bluish gray.

There were several ways of using the quills. Some were woven on a loom. Others were bent backward and forward and sewn with sinew at each turn until a flat surface of color was obtained. But before they could be used, the round quills had to be soaked in water and flattened out. Flying-Squirrel used a bone to flatten them, but Mink-Woman said that was too fussy. She held a small bundle of quills in her mouth to soften them, and flattened each one by pulling it through her clenched teeth as she needed it. There are still old Indian women who sew quills, and a piece of this work well done is more beautiful than the brightest bead work.

Flying-Squirrel made a corn-husk doll for her baby brother. She braided arms and legs and made a fat, roly-poly body with a round head. She painted a face on a piece of buckskin and sewed it to the head. Then she made a pair of leggings and a robe of soft fawn skin, so that the doll looked like a tiny warrior. The baby brother was to be a warrior some day, so the doll was hung to the large cradle-loop above his head. Beside it were tiny bows and arrows and moccasins. Looking at these things he would be inspired to run fast, shoot well, and carry himself as a warrior should.

Mink-Woman often took Flying-Squirrel fishing through the ice. Many a pickerel, bass and blue-gill came to the end of his swimming on the bone point of their spear, and fresh fish was on hand whenever anyone was hungry for it.

When early spring came with a rush, and sap crept up the trunks of trees, a great party from the village went into the maple forests for sugar. For days the woods were filled with people bringing in bark buckets of sap, which was boiled down to a thick syrup and left to harden in empty clam shells and carved wooden bowls. Two weeks of this stored up thousands of small, hard cakes of maple sugar, enough for a year.

After that came frogs singing again in the marshes, and buds, blossoms and new leaves. Mink-Woman dug herbs and secret medicines now, and taught Flying-Squirrel many things about roots and leaves. Birds returned in flocks and in pairs, and the girl learned to distinguish the song of each one.

"You were named Flying-Squirrel," said Mink-Woman one evening, "because that animal has good eyes and knows his way about the woods in the dark. Did you know that?"

"Yes, Grandmother, I know and I think that the magic of my

totem animal has crept into me, for I see in the woods very well after dark. I can run down a trail at night when Otter-Tail would stumble and fall; I can even find my way perfectly in new country, in the darkest night when there are no stars. I've done it often, berry picking and wandering in the forest."

"Ah," said Mink-Woman, "that little squirrel has given you good medicine. The day may come when it will serve you well."

One afternoon Mink-Woman decided to make a new bulrush mat for her platform. She always liked to weave her mats in the early morning while the dew was on everything.

"Dew keeps the rushes supple," she explained. "Wetting them with water doesn't do the same thing at all. They should be picked in the evening and woven in the morning. So, Flying-Squirrel, you get me some new rushes. Go over to Rush Lake, where they are thick. And remember that I want the rushes by my door before the dew is off tomorrow morning. It should not take you long to get them. Better take Willow-Girl with you for company."

The canoes had long since been taken from their mounds of sand, and Flying-Squirrel had a small canoe that she always used with Mink-Woman. It had blunt ends, was flat in the middle and would not tip easily.

"What do I want Willow-Girl for?" she said to herself. "I'm going alone." So she pushed away from the landing log.

It was a quarter-mile paddle on the big lake to a creek that flowed for a little way through a marshy place and emptied into Rush Lake. The girl reached Rush Lake just at twilight, but the dusk did not hamper her work. She lay down in the bow of the canoe and snapped the stems of the bulrushes off at the water line, piling them behind her. Every time she pulled on the rushes, her canoe slid forward, so that gradually she made a path through the thick growth.

There were clouds in the sky, and darkness came down quickly. Loons called. Ducks whipped through the reeds, squawking, and went over with a whir of wings. She could hear a loud splashing from time to time, and knew that a cow moose was feeding on lily pads in the shallow lake, and that a calf was beside her. It grew so dark she could scarcely see the other end of the canoe, but she knew what was going on all about her in the night.

At length she heard a different sort of splash, toward the creek. To you or me it might have been a moose or a deer, or a muskellunge leaping out of water. But that splash set Flying-Squirrel all a-tingle. She stopped her work and, by pulling on rushes, worked her way cautiously toward the entrance of the creek. What was that shadow on the shore, a little blacker than the trees? It came down to the creek, crouching. It was no wild animal! And then, clear and long, Flying-Squirrel heard the call of the great horned owl. But, just as the shadow was no wild animal, the girl knew that the call was not made by an owl. The hair on her head rose, and a creeping sensation went along her spine.

She tried to be calm. Perhaps it was some of the village boys playing tricks on her. She edged the canoe inshore, and crept out on a log. By inching along on her hands and knees over grass and pine needles, she came to the creek. And there she saw a man.

He was standing by a tree, his back to her. She could see his body against the gray clouds in the sky. In his hands were arrows and a bow. Even as she watched his head went back and he gave the call of the owl, "Who-whoo! Whooo! Whoooo!"

Flying-Squirrel had seen enough. This was a scout, calling in the advance guards of a war-party. She knew what it meant. Enemies were collecting to raid her own village. But she did not lose her head. It was night. She had not been discovered. She could not paddle back through the creek, but she could paddle to the other side of Rush Lake, and go on foot over the three hills that separated it from the village. She inched her way back to the place where she had left the canoe.

[41]

But the canoe was gone! Leaning far over, she saw a moccasin track on the muddy shore. Then she heard a whispered voice in the brush, another answering. She crawled out on the log and let herself down gently into the water. It crept up and up, a cold ring enclosing her body, until it touched her chin. She felt sure that she had made no ripple. She found a small, floating stump, and ducking under, came up on the other side.

Zip, thug! She had been seen or heard, after all! She did not stir. Again she heard, zip, thug! The stump heeled over a little. Against the sky she saw two arrows, still quivering, embedded in the wood. She heard a soft step on the bank, then the two voices again. There was a snicker, then a laugh. Two warriors were joking with each other about shooting at a log. Then the voices went away.

She knew that she must hurry to work her way across the lake and over the three hills that must be crossed. Pulling on rushes she went forward, still behind the stump. But the rush tops waved as she pulled and she was afraid the men would see the motion. Then she found the trail of plucked rushes she had made. She could pull on the stubs, and never show a movement.

As she went past the creek opening, inch by inch, she saw shadows leaping. The men were crossing the creek. Would they leave someone behind to look for the owner of the canoe? She could not do anything but keep going.

It seemed hours before her feet touched a mucky shore, and she pulled her body out into the thick cedar branches. It was her wits against theirs now. All her Flying-Squirrel medicine must come to her aid. She worked swiftly up one hill, over logs, through thickets, led on safely by the strange power she had described to Mink-Woman. She went through a marsh in the next hollow. The second hill was worse than the first, but she crossed it. She judged it was about midnight when she cautiously came down the slope of the third hill and saw an opening in the forest wall. The corn fields! But what was that behind that corn hill? An enemy warrior, lying full length between the rows! They had beat her to the village!

However, she knew a little, crooked path, and followed it among squash vines and pumpkins. No arrows came. Off there in the dark was a wickiup. Could she make it? She came to a pile of wood, and that gave her an idea. Why couldn't she pretend to be a girl sent out for more wood? She knew the men would not attack until early morning, and surely would not kill her now, and have the whole village warned. So she filled her arms with wood. And then, yawning and dropping a stick now and then, she walked directly toward the wickiup.

On the way she met a sentry of the village guard, who had no more idea than a chipmunk that enemies were in his territory. Flying-Squirrel whispered the news to him and, without making any reply, he walked quietly to the nearest wickiup. In the dark, word was passed from wickiup to wickiup until the whole camp was warned. With no noise, warriors armed themselves, while women and children crept out of bed and hid under the platforms. They piled baskets and bundles behind them, for protection against arrows. Would morning never come? What would happen when it did?

When Flying-Squirrel reached her wickiup and told everything to her father and Mink-Woman, Moose-Heart's jaw dropped. "Well, I'm a clam!" was all he could say. Granny folded the girl in her arms, and made her a cozy bed under the platform. But, tired as she was, for a long time she could not sleep.

All those enemy warriors strung about the camp! What a battle there would be! Finally she did sleep a little, but was wakened by a hoot from that imitation owl. Through the door she could see the gray of early morning. Would they come now?

[43]

A shrill war-whoop split the air, then another, and another. There were calls and yells, and the whole village seemed turned upside down. She heard arrows thud into the bark roof, and one came through, dangling by its feathers just above her head. But Moose-Heart and all the other men of the village were shooting to kill, and soon the war-whoops of the enemy changed to cries of fear.

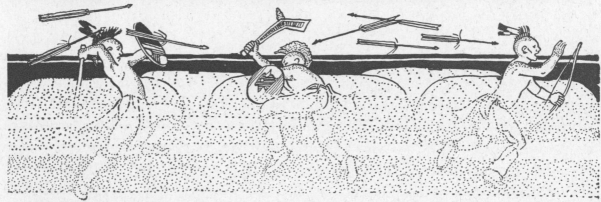

Flying-Squirrel could not stand it any longer. She ran out and saw that the village was ringed by her own people. The enemy were dropping right and left. She heard war-clubs whack on war-clubs, and there were grunts and groans. When the sun came up she saw what had happened. The enemy, instead of taking the village by surprise, had been taken by surprise themselves. Their war courage had been wiped away. Those who were alive had taken to the woods, with angry warriors from the village hot after them.

Around the fires for generations they told the story of Flying-Squirrel and her trip through the night. They had lost five men, it is true, but those men had died fighting and singing their death-songs in true, brave style; and out of the sixty enemy warriors, only seven had crossed the creek by Rush Lake and got away. The whole tribe gave a great feast in Flying-Squirrel's honor, and the dancing went on for days and days.

The village of bark wickiups was in peace, after that, for many summers.

[44]

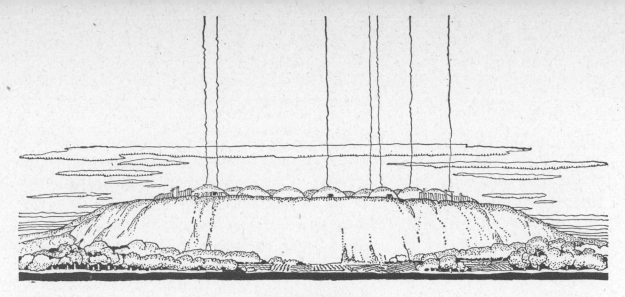

CHAPTER V

PEOPLE OF THE PLAINS

Many years before white men came to America, Buffalo-Calf lived with his mother, Elk-Woman, and his uncle, Beaver-Tail, in a village on a high bluff. The village looked down on a river and the leafy tops of cottonwoods and willows growing along its shores. There was no forest surrounding this town, as in the country of Otter-Tail and Flying-Squirrel. As far as the eye could see there was nothing but gently rolling hills covered with grass. Green in spring, yellow in summer, the land to the north, south, east and west, billowed in waves like the sea, until it touched the far, far sky. The sun danced in the grass, the wind played in it, and purple cloud shadows raced one another across its great spaces like dark eagles with spread wings.

The center of the village was a large round open space where the dance ceremonies were held. The houses were not bark wickiups, but earth lodges, ring on ring of them. They fenced in the ceremonial ground. The side of the town toward the plains was hemmed in by a tight, tall wall of posts driven into the ground. There were holes through which arrows could be shot, and little raised platforms so that spears could be thrown from the wall top, for this wall was a stockade or fort, protecting the village from enemies. On the edge of the bluff there was no wall. Enemies could not scale the steep sides of the cliff. Down below along the river bottom shimmered the long green leaves of corn, for here were the gardens.

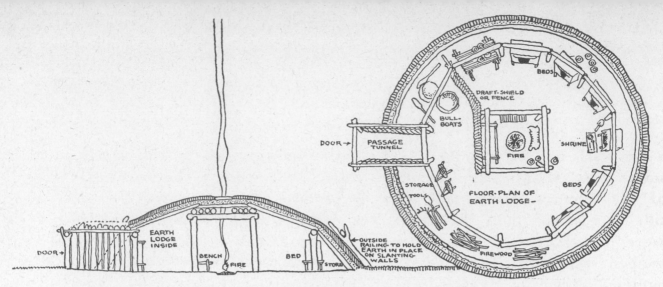

The lodges themselves looked like huge mounds of earth. The grass of the plains grew all over them in summer. In winter they were bumps of white. But from the top of each hill waved a plume of gray smoke, for these were not solid hills of clay. They were like great overturned bowls lined inside with poles and posts.

To go into Buffalo-Calf's home, you walked through a short, slanting, earth-covered tunnel, and stepped down to the floor. The room was round, and a ring of tall posts stood near the outer edges of the floor. Behind and between these posts were the family tools and furniture—hoes of buffalo shoulder blades, corn-planting sticks, rakes of elk-antlers, piles of firewood, poles, wooden mortars for pounding corn into meal, and platforms for storing food. There were bull-boats for crossing the rivers. These were like giant bowls, made of willow frames covered with buffalo hide. The beds were ranged around the room between the posts, each bed raised off the floor on willow slats and enclosed in a skin tent like a big shoe box. At the far side of the room and opposite the door was the family altar, containing the sacred medicine of the family totems.

In the center of the room in a square formed by four upright posts, the fire burned in a shallow pit. Around the fire the family squatted. Here Mother Elk-Woman made moccasins, or Uncle Beaver-Tail told stories, or Grandfather Tooth-Broken-In-The-Middle sat on a bench with his back to a draft-shield, and made arrows.

Buffalo-Calf could leave his seat by the fire, run up through the door tunnel and climb to the roof on a ladder which was just

[46]

a log with notches cut in it. He could clamber up to the square smoke hole on top, and look down inside the house on the bent back of Elk-Woman stewing elk ribs or stirring the corn mush. Outside, he could look down on the village circle, where warriors were huddled in groups talking over the affairs of the day, where women were bringing bundles of fire wood, and children and dogs tumbled about in a game of tag. Far down by the river he could see the cornfields, and girls stacking driftwood along the river bank. He could follow with his eyes the broad back of the river, squirming and bending like a lazy snake across the great plains.

Buffalo-Calf knew only this of all the world. He had never seen a great lake ribbed with rocks and pine trees, and he would have been lost in the shadows of Otter-Tail's forest. But out there where the sun would set he was going this very summer for the first time, on the great buffalo hunt!

In the days when Buffalo-Calf lived, the tribes of the plains did not wander all the year. They lived in the earth lodges, tended the gardens, and were protected by their fort walls. But every summer bands of them went wandering after the buffalo herds, "jerking" the elk and buffalo meat which would be brought home for winter food. The white man had not yet come to America, bringing the first horses with him, so the Indians walked when they traveled. They lashed their tents, or teepees, and other belongings to platforms which were fastened to two poles. These platforms, called "travois," were dragged by dogs. A dog could drag a hundred pounds or more. The teepees were made of several tanned buffalo hides sewn together and laid over a frame of poles. The materials were heavy, so the teepees had to be small enough to be dragged easily by the dogs. The poles had to be light, too, so when the teepees were put up they sagged on the poles. Later on we shall see how, when horses came to the Plains Indians, the teepees grew to be very large and sat up straight on good stiff poles.

[47]

Elk-Woman made a new teepee for the great hunt for which Uncle Beaver-Tail had brought home buffalo hides. She soaked them in mud by the river until the hair was loose and could be scraped off easily with an elk-rib scraper. Then, when the skins had been pegged out on the ground, flesh-side up, Elk-Woman and her sisters scraped off all the fat and fleshy parts with sharp scrappers made from elk bone. After this they boiled up a paste of buffalo brains and fat and bone grease, and spread it thickly over the skins. After a day or so they washed the skins clean with warm water and hung them to dry. Then they rubbed and twisted and pulled each skin over a sharp-edged beam. Buffalo-Calf helped as much as he could, but his arms soon ached for it was hard work. When it was over, the skins were tanned leather, soft and white.

Elk-Woman laid out seven skins and, dipping her fingers into red paint, with a dot here and there she marked how they were to be cut. The women cut them and sewed the pieces together into one big sheet. They used sinew thread, taken from the tendon that runs along a buffalo's backbone. This sinew could be shredded to any thickness, and the shredding was Buffalo-Calf's job. Instead of using needles, the women made holes in the skin with bone awls and pushed the sinew through the holes. The sinew was used wet. When it dried it would never break.

After all the pieces had been sewed together they made a teepee in the form of a half moon. At one edge two smoke flaps were sewn. When the tent had been put up on the pole frame and weighted all around the bottom with stones, the smoke flaps were kept in place with poles. These flaps took the place of the dampers used in chimneys today. They could be adjusted for any wind so that the smoke from a fire in the center of the teepee floor would rise straight up and go out at the top, instead of circling around inside.

[48]

Buffalo-Calf knew only this of all the world. *See page 47.*

When enough teepees were finished, three hundred people gathered together for the fall hunt. The warriors and hunters wore buckskin leggings and moccasins shimmering with porcupine quills. They carried clubs, tomahawks, knives, lances, and spears, as well as bows and great sheaves of arrows in quivers.

The women rounded up their several hundred dogs, and what a noise there was while the packing was being done! The travois poles were brought out from the store places in the earth lodges and tied to the dogs. Then packs, bundles, teepees, sacks of corn meal, cooking pots, ladles, buffalo-horn spoons, fleshing knives, plenty of extra flint, and all the gew-gaws and knickknacks needed for two or three months of wandering were lashed to the travois. The Indians had had long dances for the success of the hunt, and the Medicine Men had worked all the magic tricks they knew to insure a safe journey and a safe return. Finally the procession moved off.

[49]

The stay-at-homes, who were to tend the gardens and protect the village, crowded the roofs of the earth lodges to see the departure. From the center of town the hunting party marched between the lodges, through the pole gate of the fort wall, and out across the yellow grass toward the setting sun. Men shouted, women called, children scampered and squealed and got lost in the crowd. When they found their way back to their families they were tied safely on their own travois behind the strong dogs. The dogs barked and howled and wagged their tails and bent forward in the harness. The dragging poles of the travois made a swishing sound. Dust sprang into the warm air in an ever-rising cloud. This river of people was soon lost to those on the roofs, in the long grass and dust.

Buffalo-Calf was in the procession, striding along beside the big dog who carried his baby brother, surrounded by the pots for the family cooking. Up ahead he could see the backs of dogs, their tails curled up. Here and there in the midst of dust, a feather nodded where a brave walked. Behind him strode other people, and the heads of panting dogs swayed from side to side as they pulled forward.

So Buffalo-Calf went on the great hunt.

CHAPTER VI

BUFFALO-CALF AND THE GREAT HERD

The hunting party marched like an army. Far ahead went the scouts to look for game and water. Behind them, leading the procession, walked four old chiefs, the wisest in the band. They carried the sacred pipes and medicine bundles of the tribe to ward off evil. They were the ones who would say where camps were to be made and when the hunt was to be started. Next came the women and children, with the dogs—a long string of them. But only one out of every four dogs dragged a travois. The others were taken to relieve these, and to bring back the great meat supplies that the tribe hoped to have after the hunt. On each side and at the rear of this baggage train walked heavily armed warriors, so that in case of enemy attack the women, children and baggage would be protected. But, according to the scouts, there were no enemies in the country, this season.

The procession covered only ten miles the first day, because they had started late. In the afternoon the four old chiefs halted on the edge of a winding river. "Here we camp," they said. The dogs seemed to know the words, for the loaded ones dropped, panting, in the grass. Women and children scrambled over them, slipping the harness and unlashing the baggage from the travois poles. What happy dogs they were! They rolled in the grass, scratched, and stretched themselves. Then they raced after the others to lap water greedily.

On a slope a little higher than the surrounding country, tripods of willow poles rose like magic in the grass. Other poles were leaned against these until pointed frames sprouted all over the place. There was a great flapping of teepee covers when they were being put up. It seemed as though gigantic brown, white and yellow birds were either alighting or flying away.

Buffalo-Calf and his friends had been sent to find rocks. Away to the river bank they raced, where round, water-worn boulders poked up through the clay among old buffalo skulls and bones. Here they gathered stones the size of a child's head and laid them on buffalo hides. Dogs were caught and hitched to these with thongs. The hides were dragged easily over the slippery grass.

When Buffalo-Calf came up the slope again, watching to make sure that the stones did not slide off the hide, the teepees were up. They were about ten feet high, on the inside, and the heavy sides sagged inward, sloping out again at the base. The bottom edges of the teepee covers lay flat on the ground, and the stones brought by the children were set around them, anchoring the covers down.

The camp was planned well. In the center were the teepees of the four chiefs and their families. The rest of the teepees were grouped around these in a circle-within-a-circle. All the doors faced east. When the smoke flaps were fitted with their poles, they stuck out like great ears against the sky.

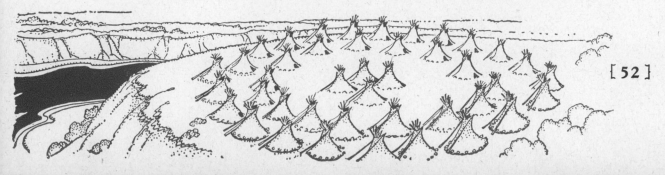

Firemaking among all Indians was an art. In some tribes sacred fires were lighted by a circle of warriors or chiefs who took turns spinning a round stick between their palms, back and forth. The lower end of the stick was pointed and drilled into a shallow pit in a small board on the ground. Friction between the point of the stick, or drill, and the board produced a brown powder and wisps of smoke. When the powder turned jet black and smoked in little clouds, the drill was removed and the powder fanned. Then a red coal appeared, no larger than a sparrow's eye. Fine grass or bark tinder, laid on this, was soon blown into a flame. But this method took a long time and was used only for sacred fires.

An easier way was to wind once, about the drill, a thong, of which the ends were fastened to the tips of a bent stick. The top of the drill was held steady against a stone grip and the bent stick was sawed back and forth. The thong spun the drill much faster than human hands could do. Thus the coal could be made in a half minute, or less.

Cooking fires were built outside the teepees. First a circle of grass was burned away, so that there was no danger of starting a prairie fire. In the center of the burned patch the fire was laid. Along the river bank were pieces of driftwood, but as no trees grew near by, "buffalo chips" were used for fuel. All over the plains, and especially in the deep trails and along river bottoms, these gray, sun-dried cakes were scattered.

"See what a great brother the buffalo is," said Mother Elk-Woman as her son led in a dog dragging a hideful of chips. "He gives us not only our teepees, but our food and sleeping robes. From his bones we make tools and weapon points. From his horns, bows. Glue comes from his hoofs. He carries his own tanning material for the hide, his own sewing thread and bone awls. And the grass he eats, packed tight in his droppings, dries into light, firm chips to make the finest fuel."

[53]

The evening meal of boiled jerked meat was cooked quickly. By the time it had been eaten the sun was a round red coal burning its way into the world in the west. Then, with warrior sentries posted about the teepee circle, the tired people lay down on their robes. Buffalo-Calf was so excited he could hardly sleep. He was on the Great Hunt at last! He was sure that he could hear the thunder of buffalo hoofs drumming the ground beneath his ear. Or was it only the thousands of crickets singing? He closed his eyes—for just a minute, it seemed—but when he opened them again, the camp was gray in the first faint light of early morning.

With breakfast over, they broke camp. Dogs barked, children called, poles clattered down. The teepees were made into neat bundles of covers and poles before Buffalo-Calf realized what it was all about. Why all the hurry? The chiefs had decided to make thirty miles before dark, straight west. So, when the new sun blinked his yellow eye on the train, he saw only their backs, for they were already on the move. Behind them on the slope were nothing but patches of burned grass and rings of teepee stones.*

The plains were cut across in all directions by game trails, made mostly by the buffalo. These trails were a foot or two wide, and often two feet deep. Here and there in the grass beside the trails gleamed the chalky white bones and skulls of animals that had died of old age in winter, or had been killed by gray wolves.

"With so many buffalo in sight all the time," said Buffalo-Calf to his Uncle Beaver-Tail, "why can't the hunters just go out and shoot them with arrows?"

"The trouble is," replied Beaver-Tail, "that there are too many. If one of them sees a hunter and gives the alarm by running, soon all the animals are following in a great stampede. They may run for forty miles and not leave a single buffalo for us to hunt. If only The Great Spirit had given the Indians a large dog to ride on, so that we could run after them! But we must do everything

[54]

* If you ever fly in a plane from St. Paul, Minnesota, to Miles City, Montana, look for these stone rings in South Dakota. The white stones stand out against the dark sod, if you are flying low and look straight down. Each ring is about twelve feet across, and together they form the circle-in-a-circle of the old teepee camps.

on foot. Thus we must band together and take a great herd all at once. From time to time our hunters dress in the skins of wolves and stalk the buffalo through the grass and sage. Buffalo do not bother much with wolves unless they come in a pack and attack the calves. So a hunter often gets within bowshot of a buffalo here and there. But the great herd we must take all at once, or our people go without buffalo meat through the winter."

"And how is this great herd to be taken?" asked Buffalo-Calf.

"Be patient, and you will see," returned Beaver-Tail, leaving the boy to wonder as he trudged along beside the dogs.

Several days later the scouts came in with reports, and the four chiefs ordered a change in the direction of the march. The column turned sharply to the north.

"Ah," said Beaver-Tail. "We are going to the big bluff on the large river this season. I haven't been there for years. There's a good buffalo trap there."

"A buffalo trap? Can you catch a buffalo in a snare or a deadfall?" asked the boy. His uncle did not reply, but the next day Buffalo-Calf saw the trap. They were winding their way along the shore of the river, where thickets of willow and cottonwoods grew. When they came to a bluff two hundred feet high, they marched around it and made their camp at its base.

Then Beaver-Tail led his nephew farther along to a place directly below the highest part of the bluff. Here was a tangle of driftwood logs and rocks, making a pen almost as large as their whole camp circle. Buffalo-Calf clambered over the logs. Inside, the ground was white with bones! Thousands of them!

"This is the buffalo trap," said Beaver-Tail. "Many a great herd has been taken here. All you have to do is run the buffalo over the cliff, and they topple two hundred feet down to their deaths."

Buffalo-Calf looked up the steep clay and rock bluff. "It sounds

[55]

easy," he said, "but suppose the buffalo want to run the other way instead of toward the cliff?"

"You'll see how it is done, and soon," his uncle promised, "for I am to be the Buffalo-Caller, and you will be my scout. So take your sleeping robe and some dried meat and a good long drink of water, and we'll climb up to the top of the bluff."

On top of the bluff, Buffalo-Calf saw a strange arrangement. Hills of rock and sod, grown over with grass and weeds, had been built years before. The hills would hide from two to five men apiece. They were placed in two long lines, beginning at the edge of the cliff and branching out in a fan shape. The two hills at the edge of the cliff were about three hundred feet apart. The two at the other end of the long lines were over a half mile apart, so that they marked out a piece of land shaped like a funnel. The lines were each a half mile long and the hills in each line about thirty feet apart.

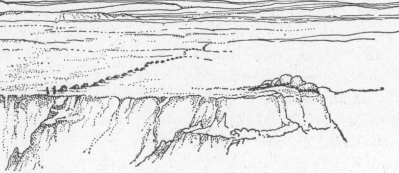

"Simple, isn't it?" said Beaver-Tail.

"I suppose so, if you know what it's about," said Buffalo-Calf. "And now what do I do?"

"You stay behind this first rock pile," his uncle said. "I will go out to the last one on the right hand line. When the right kind of herd grazes in this direction, I'll wave my robe. Then you wave yours to signal the camp." And with no more explanation, Beaver-Tail walked quickly out over the plain.

Buffalo-Calf sprawled over the top of the hill nearest him. A few scraggly bushes of sage grew here, their gray trunks gnarled and twisted like the trunks of dwarf trees. Looking through their branches the boy could see the open plain, sloping gently down from the horizon.

Far across the yellow plain the boy saw flashes of white. He knew that they were antelope, signaling danger by flirting the long white hair on their rumps. This caught the sun and warned other antelope, who signaled in turn. Had they seen Uncle Beaver-Tail? No—they were on guard against coyotes! Buffalo-Calf knew how two coyotes would run an antelope, first one hiding in the brush while the other drove the frightened beast in a circle. When the first one had brought the antelope back, after a run of many miles, the second coyote would take up the chase while the first one rested. And thus the fleetest animal of the plains would become exhausted and be brought down in the end.

The day wore slowly on. Eagles soared in the sky, crickets sang their monotonous chant. Gophers and mice played among the grasses and sage clumps. But the buffalo were far away—only a thin, black line low on the horizon. When night came, a boy from camp brought up a pot of clear drinking water, and after a supper of dried meat, Buffalo-Calf curled up and went to sleep.

It was several days before the herds moved into this territory, and all the time Buffalo-Calf and his uncle stayed on guard. The thin dark line of animals wound slowly toward the bluff, in and out of hollows. The line broke apart and became beads, the beads rolled together again to become black and brown masses. Thousands of animals were out there on the plain. At length a part of the herd, numbering many hundreds, broke away and began to graze straight toward the two lines of hills!

All through the day Buffalo-Calf was on the alert, and finally he saw a wave of Beaver-Tail's robe. Creeping backward through the grass so carefully that a cricket on his bare back didn't jump off, he

[57]

waited until he was well below the edge of the bluff, then he waved his robe until he was sure the people in the camp below had seen his signal.

Soon the camp was in action. The dogs were tied up to trees so they would not spoil the hunt, and men, women and children began climbing the bluff. Each person carried a robe or a large white deer hide. Nobody spoke a word, but at the top of the bluff they separated into two groups. Each group crept along one of the lines of mounds, taking their places behind the hills until each hill screened two or three persons. It was done quickly, and to Buffalo-Calf it seemed as though the prairie ate them up. Soon there was no movement to be seen anywhere. To look at the bluff, you would not know that there was a human being within miles.

The buffalo herd was still three miles away, grazing slowly. And then the boy saw Beaver-Tail. He was out on the plain, between the two farthest hills. The boy thought him a buffalo at first, for, with a buffalo robe over him, and its stuffed head wagging from side to side, he looked very much like one. To the herd, when the animals first sighted him, he must have looked the same.

After a while, an old cow began to wonder at the odd animal all alone on a rise of ground. She left the herd slowly and grazed toward it, lifting her head from time to time. Then she walked forward and stopped. Another cow from the herd joined her, then another. Finally most of the herd were gazing wonderingly at Beaver-Tail. After a time they became restless. Was this a buffalo or wasn't it? They moved in at a walk, faster and faster, until the first old cow was trotting.

Still a distance separated Beaver-Tail from the cow, perhaps a quarter of a mile. The imitation buffalo ducked down in a coulee, came up on another rise and pretended to graze. Then he did an odd dance, ducking this way and that, and making strange noises, all the time moving slowly toward the edge of the cliff. By this time the cow was well inside the outer opening of the funnel of hills. Two

[58]

calves trotted after, then more cows. A big bull followed, heavy horns peeping from thick brown mane, his flanks slate gray. Then came buffalo after buffalo, all intent on that queer thing in front of them.

Now Beaver-Tail was running between the two lines of hills. The buffalo were gaining on him, but only the first few animals could see him. The middle and rear of the herd trotted along wondering what it was all about, but feeling that they should keep up in the excitement. Overhead, some still clinging to the woolly backs, came the buffalo birds that pick the flies and ticks from the great beasts and wander everywhere with them. A cloud of dust rolled up. Hundreds of pounding feet thundered.

When the herd was well inside the outer picket lines, the Indians from the farthest hills began hopping out from their hiding places, yelling and shrieking, and waving their robes. As the last of the herd passed each hill, more Indians bobbed out, waving frantically. The last buffalo were panic-stricken. They pressed forward faster and faster, but the faster they went, the more Indians popped out of the very ground and waved them on.

This was too much for the buffalo. Those behind forgot everything but mad flight forward. The whole herd was terrorized. Beaver-
Tail had long since slid into the tall grass and run to Buffalo-Calf's
hill. And now, blind to everything, thinking only of getting away,
the whole herd thundered past the rock piles. In a steady stream of
dark bodies the buffalo went over the cliff, to fall dead on the rocks
two hundred feet below.

"And that is a buffalo drive," said Beaver-Tail to Buffalo-Calf,
who was trembling with excitement. The man was wrapping up his
buffalo robe, breathing hard from his long run, and perspiring in
streams. "Now our tribe has meat and robes and everything to make
it happy for another year. We have taken over four hundred buffalo, enough to last us through the winter. And now let us go down
and help with the skinning."

[60]

CHAPTER VII

IN THE DAYS OF RIDES-AWAY-TINKLING

Now we are going to skip over a hundred years. Buffalo-Calf grew up to be a brave warrior and hunter, like his uncle Beaver-Tail. He had children and grandchildren and great-grandchildren and finally he went to join his ancestors in the Happy Hunting Grounds. Meanwhile the village grew so large that it could not be one village any longer, so the people divided into two tribes. One of these tribes went away to the west, toward great mountains. And then the white man came to America.

The Spaniards, far, far south, in Mexico, brought horses from Europe, and the horses had colts that grew up, until there were great herds of horses. Some of the herds broke away from their masters and fled into the hills, where new colts were born. And a hundred years after the buffalo hunt you read about in the last chapter, herds of wild horses wandered in the Rocky Mountains and across the Great Plains, along with the buffalo, the elk, and the antelope. Mexican Indians learned to ride from seeing the Spaniards, and other Indians farther north learned from them.

What a new idea this was! Instead of walking weary miles, one could sit on a horse and go here, there, anywhere. Men could ride farther in one day than they could walk in five, and could carry with them heavier material than could ever be pulled by dogs. The new idea spread among the tribes like wildfire. Horses were given away, traded, stolen; and soon the tribe which had broken away from Buffalo-Calf's village had horses and changed its habits completely.

"What need, now," they said, "to huddle in one place in dark and gloomy earth lodges. We have the wings of the wind to carry us anywhere." So they left their lodges to be washed away by the rain or torn down by the winds, and they had no need of a fort any more.

The great-grandchildren of Buffalo-Calf had gone with this new tribe, and one of the families descended from them had a beautiful daughter named Rides-Away-Tinkling. Just as her ancestor, Buffalo-Calf, had helped his mother make a teepee, she now helped her mother make one; but that early teepee had been made of only seven buffalo-hides—a tiny shelter that wobbled on its bending poles. Now the teepee on which Rides-Away-Tinkling worked had *twenty* skins. It was the largest in the tribe! A wiry, strong mustang dragged it on a travois, just as the dogs had dragged the smaller teepee. It was exactly the same shape, but the poles were longer, and the round frame for carrying it was bigger. When this teepee was put up it stood on stout, strong poles, straight as a bowstring, and the edge of the big tent sat squarely on the ground without a sag or ripple.

Rides-Away-Tinkling had never seen a white man. Most of her people could only guess what one looked like. They had never yet seen a wagon on wheels. But some of the bravest men had journeyed far to the south on their horses, loaded with beaver furs, and had traded with these odd people face to face. For a pile of skins as high as their knees, they had bought an iron knife! For a pile as tall as their belts, they had been given a tomahawk with a steel head! And for other piles, glass beads as small as the eyes of mice, with holes clear through them so they could be sewn in designs like porcupine quill-work, only much faster. Just think! For only as many thick beaver skins as a very strong horse could carry, one could buy a whole basket of these beads—bright red, yellow, blue, white, black.

Rides-Away-Tinkling's father, Many-Painted-Ponies, had been one of these brave men, not afraid of those white persons. He was a good bargainer, too. Nobody could get the better of him, he said. Why, for only fifty horses and the pelts from five years of hard trapping, he had come home loaded with presents for his friends and family! His women folk had all the beads they needed for their white buckskin dresses, and his boys had red cloth—think of it—for their breech-cloths! Not only that, but he brought his beautiful daughter a gift which gave her her name. It was ten tiny brass bells. She tied them tightly to her best dress, below the belt, with strong thongs. And when she climbed into her bright saddle on her spotted pony and rode away, the whole tribe heard her—for she rode away, tinkling!

But the crowning glory was something her father kept for himself. It was a tube of bright metal, fixed onto a piece of wood. He took some black powder from a funny new kind of horn. He rammed it down with a stick and a patch of buckskin. After ramming down some round pieces of a heavy metal, and pulling a little stick at the bottom of the wood, he made thunder and lightning, and a buffalo fell dead at a greater distance than it would have been possible to shoot him with an arrow! Rides-Away-Tinkling's father had tried it out, on the journey back. No more bows and arrows for him, he said.

So he assembled all his friends on the outskirts of the big circle of teepees, and made them a speech about the new magic. He also brought out his bow and his arrows and gave them away. Then he took up his new weapon, and everybody was impressed, though they didn't say much. He opened the magic horn and poured the powder into the metal tube. He kept pouring till he was sure there was enough. Then he pulled the little stick.

[63]

Such a thunder! Lightning split the air! A great cloud of bad-smelling smoke rolled up. When his friends saw Many-Painted-Ponies again, he was sitting down in the grass, looking at his magic stick. Something had gone wrong. The metal tube was bent and full of cracks. It never killed a buffalo after that, but Many-Painted-Ponies always hooked the bent metal over his shoulder in the dances, and people would say: "He has one of those White-Man-Magic-Sticks." This made him a greater chief than ever.

That was the first gun these people had ever heard. They were not to hear another for many years. They lived on the plains, happy without guns. But one magic of the white man they did have, and that was the horse. No matter where the buffalo went now, the Indians could follow him on the wings of the wind, from the open plains to the Rocky Mountains.

The tribe of Rides-Away-Tinkling had wandered over the eastern part of the Great Plains during the summer. Now it was moving west again. The string of horses seemed endless. Black ponies, white ponies, bay, brown and "painted" ones, spotted in two or more colors —all trotted along over the yellow prairie.

As in the days of long ago, when on the march, women and children made the central column. With them were horses, using the same sort of travois that the dogs had used, but of course much larger. Herd boys in the rear took care of the many extra horses. In front rode the chiefs, as before. There was the same formation of warriors at the sides and rear as a guard, and far out ahead, miles in advance, rode the scouts.

The great train was now passing a low bluff. On this bluff, against the sky, low, rambling mounds stood out. Rides-Away-Tinkling, at a sign from her father, left the women, rode out through the warriors and met him trotting toward these mounds.

Rides-Away-Tinkling, at a sign from her father, rode out and met him. *See page 64.*

"Here, my daughter, is an abandoned village such as our people used in the days before we had horses," her father said, drawing in beside her until their stirrups touched. "Your great ancestor, Buffalo-Calf, lived in just such a village."

"But isn't his tribe still alive?" asked Rides-Away-Tinkling.

"Oh, yes," replied Many-Painted-Ponies, "and the people still live in their earth lodges farther east on the Great River, the Missouri. But even those lodges have changed since Buffalo-Calf was a boy. With the coming of horses they became larger. Now in one lodge there is room, not only for a family and relatives, but also, sometimes, for as many as twenty of the best ponies. But this ancient village we're coming to was built in the days when its inhabitants had only dogs as beasts of burden. I want you to look over the ruins, to see how times have changed since then."

They reined in their horses on a knoll and looked down. A few gray poles poked upward through the sod, all that was left of the stockade. The roofs of the lodges had fallen in, but some of the sturdy center poles still stood upright. Earth from the roofs had made low hills over which grass grew, and running in and out among the mounds were the hard-packed trails of buffalo.

"How lonely it looks," said Rides-Away-Tinkling. "It is hard to believe that this used to be a village inhabited by people who walked far out on the plains, slaughtering as many buffalo as was possible at one time, dragging the dried meat home with the dogs. And now the buffalo walk through its streets. Life must have been very hard in those days."

"Yes, it was a hard life," replied Many-Painted-Ponies, "but it was a good life, too. A man had to be as hard as my iron knife then. He had to be a good walker, and a good runner. I have heard tales of how Buffalo-Calf, when he grew to manhood, ran eighty miles between sunrise and sunrise, on a bet. The course was out to a hunting camp and back, forty miles each way. When he came sprinting through the stockade gates, the people cheered from the lodge roofs. Straight to the dancing circle he ran, and, to show off, leaped over a pile of buffalo skulls. He landed right in a puddle of mud, but he did not mind the laugh this caused because he knew that no one else in the tribe could have done what he had done. He won twelve big dogs on that bet.

"In these days," he went on, "what do our warriors do now? Ride! Ride! It's hard to make one of our young men walk twenty feet, if there is a horse handy. Of course they can fight and ride for a week at a time, changing horse at the camps and eating in the saddle; but what is that compared to men like Buffalo-Calf? The horse is a wonderful animal, but it is making soft meat of our men. Perhaps, after all, the good old days were the best!"

"Well, Father," replied Rides-Away-Tinkling with a smile at the corners of her mouth, "if you think walking such healthful exercise, look out there. Our train is just a line in the distance. Now, I'll lead your horse, and you can trot back on foot. You might catch up by morning."

"Making fun of your father, are you?" said Many-Painted-Ponies, pretending to be angry. "And that's another thing. The younger generation is getting more disrespectful every day."

"Anyway," said Rides-Away-Tinkling, "I'm glad I'm alive now. I wouldn't like to live in a dark, dingy old earth lodge, having known the fresh air of our teepee, or to stay in one place by a corn patch all my life. I would die if we couldn't ride and ride, seeing new country, new mountains, new lakes! Come on, I'll beat you back to the others!" And with a slap of quirts, the ponies spurted forward over the plain.

Two weeks later the tribe had reached the foothill country. Already in the west the great ranges of the Rocky Mountains lay blue against the sky. Many-Painted-Ponies came into camp one morning, and gathered the other chiefs about him in his teepee.

"Good buffalo country here," he said. "All around the open plain

before us are ravines and arroyos. We could surround a herd out there without being seen by the buffalo. We need fresh meat now and we can store supplies of dried meat here for use when we come back this way next winter or spring. Besides, it's time the women were making pemmican."

"He speaks with a wise tongue," said Sleeps-In-The-Saddle, taking his turn at the passed-around pipe. So a hunt was decided upon.

Camp was pitched in a river valley out of sight of the open country. The teepees were white specks in the thickets of willows and cottonwoods. The horses were hidden down in low grass lands. With nothing in sight for days, the buffalo, which had fled before the moving Indians, began drifting back into the country.

One night Many-Painted-Ponies said it was time for the hunt, and, leading a party, he started out.

When the right herd came along, they rode quietly along the bottoms of the coulees, and by morning they had surrounded the buffalo. At a signal of smoke from a watcher on a high butte, they began to close in. Each man covered his head with a buffalo robe and, drawing the corners together, sat on them so that the skin could not slip off. As they let their horses graze toward the herd, they sprawled over the necks of the ponies. Thus they looked like humped buffalo, and the animals took no alarm. An hour passed, then another. At length

the buffalo sensed something wrong. They became restless and the watcher on the butte knew that at any moment they might stampede. He gave the signal for the attack and the riders trotted forward.

The buffalo did not know which way to turn. In every direction there were riders. The outer animals headed for the middle, and all milled about in confusion. Then the men threw back their robes and charged down the flanks of the herd, pouring arrows into the mass of brown bodies as fast as they could notch them. The buffalo broke and ran in all directions. The horses were fresh. Their riders steered them by knee pressure only, keeping both hands free for their weapons. It was every man for himself, and each rider followed a certain group.

Rides-Away-Tinkling sat on a hill and watched. First she saw the herd like a brown puddle of mud on the yellow plain. When the riders charged, it was as though some giant had thrown a great stone that made the puddle splash out at the edges in all directions. She saw a horse close in beside a buffalo. She saw the bow drawn, saw it snap taut again. The buffalo plunged forward and went down. Then the horse spurted forward again to range alongside another buffalo.

They were dropping by dozens now. When the arrows were all gone, men used their lances. The tide of brown surged across a flat place, and when it had gone the ground was dotted with dark mounds. From the hill where Rides-Away-Tinkling watched, these mounds looked like strings of beads, all pointing outward from the place where the herd had first stood.

Now the women and children came galloping from camp, and the business of skinning began. When elk and deer were to be skinned, they were hoisted up on poles. But a cow buffalo weighed about a thousand pounds, and the bulls sometimes a ton, so the easiest way to skin them was to slit the hide along the backbone as the animal lay on its side, and work the skin off the upper side and under the belly. When this had been done, the meat from that side was removed. Then the buffalo could be turned over, and the remaining hide and meat taken off.

All that week the meat was dried in strips in the sun or cured over smoking fires. When it was thoroughly dried it was hard and weighed less than half as much as when it was fresh. The large leg bones were crushed with stone hammers, and the marrow and "bone grease" boiled in pots and skimmed off. Some of this was stored in cleaned bladders and intestines. Some was used in making pemmican.

To make pemmican, the women pounded the dried meat with stone hammers until it was in fine shreds. Then they mixed it with dried berries which had been gathered and stored for this purpose. Finally they mixed with it some of the bone grease, and put the paste up in the bladder and intestine casings. It would keep for three or four years, and was prized as a winter food. One spoonful made a meal, rich and well balanced.

Enough meat to last for a journey was stored in "parfleches." These were rawhide covered bundles, folded like a flat suitcase, which were to be carried with the tribe on its wanderings. The remainder was to be left behind.

Many-Painted-Ponies superintended this job. Men marked out certain spots on bluffs, and cut at each spot a circle of sod two feet

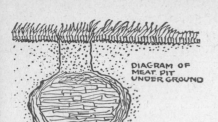

across. They lifted the sod out carefully and laid it aside. Then they dug straight down, as though making a hole for a huge post. Two feet down they began scooping outward all around until they had a den like a great pot large enough to hold two men. They dug with buffalo shoulder blades, and handed the dirt up in pots and baskets through the two foot "man-hole."

When the den was large enough, they lined it with willow brush, dry grass and finally dry hides. Then they climbed out and the jerked meat was laid inside and covered with grass, hides and earth. The hole was filled with earth, well packed down, and the sod cover put back exactly in place. All the earth dug from the den had been kept in hides, and what was left over was thrown into the river.

"Now," said Many-Painted-Ponies to his daughter, "the coyotes and wolves will gnaw the bones down on the plain, but they will not find these storehouses. Neither will our enemies. The meat will keep perfectly for a year or two, and we can always return to this spot if we need food in our wanderings."

The week after the storing of the dried buffalo meat, the tribe reached the Rocky Mountains. Here they would camp through the fall, hunting and trapping for furs along the lakes and streams. But, here is an odd thing. With all the lakes and rivers alive with fish, these Indians would not think of eating them. A good Plains Indian considered buffalo, elk, moose and deer fit for men and warriors. But fish? Never!

To the northwest lay the Country of Smokes, which we know as Yellowstone Park. The Indians regarded it with awe. Through cracks in the earth, giants breathed steam and hot water that sprayed the very skies. There were places where mud bubbled forever in mighty cauldrons. It was a place of evil spirits! But, also in this place lay the Mountain-of-Black-Ice, a mound of obsidion, which made the best arrow points and knives. A few men had iron knives in the tribe, but iron was too precious to be wasted on arrow points.

[70]

FLAKING OBSIDION
ARROW POINTS WITH
TOOL OF DEER ANTLER.

Many-Spotted-Ponies volunteered to lead a party into the Country-of-Smokes for this black ice. Rides-Away-Tinkling pleaded to be taken, but her father only laughed. Of course no girl child could go on such a dangerous mission among evil spirits, he said. But he liked to have his daughter by his side and finally he gave in.

"I think your medicine is strong enough to bring you back safely;" he said, "but, just to be sure, we will have the chief medicine man make you a mighty charm to carry."

He paid two horses for the most powerful charm the medicine man could make, and Rides-Away-Tinkling rode with the men. They passed through a region where the three great peaks of the Teton Mountains in Wyoming towered against the sky. They left the sage brush country and entered a pine forest. They passed a long lake and a mighty river which fell over a great cliff to roar down the deep, deep canyon of the Yellowstone. They wandered over high mountains, where the girl could see what she thought was the whole world spread below her. Finally they came to the Mountain-of-Black-Ice.

Here they gathered pieces of the volcanic glass, and packed them carefully in leather sacks on the pack horses. Then they turned to go back, for no Indian liked to stay long in this evil country. But the geysers, those spouting holes where hot water was flung into the sky, did not frighten Rides-Away-Tinkling. She was not frightened by anything. Did she not wear on her string of beads a charm for which her father had paid two horses?

So she stayed behind, watching a great plain smoking with steam. When she looked around there was not a living thing in sight. She knew at once what had happened. Steam from the many geysers had hidden the riders and their horses, and her own horse must have wandered away and been lost to sight in the same way. There were tracks of horses in a muddy place, and she followed them. Surely as soon as her father missed her he would ride back.

But she followed the tracks for a whole day without sight of any

living creature. Though she was lost, she had a wonderful time. She saw a canyon where rocks stood up like giants, and she reached a place where hot water poured over rocks to form terraces of pink and purple and bright red. (This is the place we call Mammoth Hot Springs.) She slept that night on earth that was warm, beneath whispering pines, and no evil spirits came to mar her dreams, and nothing harmed her.

Early in the morning she was awakened by the sound of galloping hoofs, and there was her father, quite pale, looking anxiously down at her from his horse. Hurt? Of course not! And where had her father been all this time?

Many-Spotted-Ponies dismounted and, sitting beside, her, told a story which, like all the country about them, seemed a fairy tale. She had been screened by a smoking geyser, he said, just at the moment when a band of enemy warriors had closed in on the party. Her father and his companions had drawn them down a canyon and, after a battle in which three men of his party had been wounded, they had beaten the other band and taken six scalps and many horses, with full war gear! Rides-Away-Tinkling had followed the tracks of still another party in the wrong direction!

But it was all over now. That geyser had probably saved her life. She got on her father's horse behind him, and together they found their band and wound through the mountains back to the big camp. She was the envy of all her friends, for she had seen things unbelievable. This trip set her quite apart in the tribe, for she had led a charmed life in the evil country. When she grew up, her people gave her a new name. It was no more Rides-Away-Tinkling, but Woman-No-Spirits-Can-Harm.

[72]

CHAPTER VIII
PEOPLE OF THE DESERTS AND MESAS

The Desert Country of New Mexico and Arizona is a land of sun and bright color. The Rocky Mountains come down from the north, and spread out over the desert like fingers. Between these mountain fingers the land looks flat, but it is all criss-crossed with deep canyons. Ages ago, before this country was a desert, great rivers scooped out these canyons. One of them, the Grand Canyon of the Colorado River, is the largest and deepest crack to be found in the whole world. The river at the bottom of the Grand Canyon still runs. But most of the others are long since dry.

The land between these old river beds is now left standing up above the canyon bottoms like huge tables. The word "mesa" is Spanish for "table" and that is what these formations are called. Some are as big as a house, others as large as a whole county. The sides of these mesas and the canyon walls show rocks of many colors, in layers, like a cake that has been cut. Many of the layers are red or yellow, but most of the colors of the rainbow can be seen here when the sun strikes the rocks.

On some of the mountain tops snow lies for half the year. This melts and forms brooks, which carry to the desert rivers the scanty supply of water they now have. On the mountains, pines, spruces and cedar trees grow. Many plants grow even on the mesa tops, in the hottest and dryest parts of the desert. There are hundreds of different kinds of cacti. Most of these have bright flowers, and fruits which men and animals can eat, but the body of the cactus is protected by thousands of sharp thorns. Another plant that grows here is the "yucca" which sprays its long leaves in every direction like a pin cushion with the pins pointed outward. There are many varieties.

In some places sage grows. Cottonwood trees and willows follow the canyon streams. Where water flows, grass grows, for the soil of the desert is very fertile. Given plenty of water, it grows anything.

GIANT CACTUS

CHOLLA CACTUS (PRONOUNCED CHOY-AH)

PRICKLY-PEAR CACTUS

3 KINDS OF YUCCA

[73]

In this hot, dry desert country, many creatures live. In the rivers are fish, turtles and frogs. The rattlesnake coils on the hot rocks in the sun. Little lizards of blue and green scurry zigzag up canyon walls. The gila monster clambers stupidly over stones. He has an orange coat banded with black, and looks as though some Indian Spirit had embroidered him all over with heavy beads. Harmless horned toads scuttle, burrowing into the sand.

Along the rivers a few ducks swim, but this is not a country for water birds. Instead a true desert bird, the road-runner, patters over the mesas in search of lizards and snakes for dinner. Thin, trim little hawks and owls fat as butter-balls perch on the cactus. Song-birds warble from bush and sage. Wild turkeys gobble from the pine ridges. Over the mountains the great eagle soars, and far up in the turquoise sky wheels the vulture, ever watching for a dead antelope or deer.

In the old days buffalo came to the eastern edges of the desert, but there was not enough grass for their huge herds. Today there are bears, wolves, and foxes, just as in the long ago, and coyotes still sit in the sage to yip and howl at the full moon. Cottontails and jack-rabbits play up and down the arroyos, and when the coyote goes yapping across the mesa top, whole villages of prairie dogs vanish down their burrows.

So, you see, though at first a desert seems to be a very desolate place, it really is quite alive. If you know its secrets you can live in it comfortably. If you do not, you may die, for the windstorms sweep across its wastes, swirling dust and sand to wipe out the trail. Mirages—sky-pictures caused by the heat-waves—lure you toward lakes and rivers that do not exist. And water is hard to find.

The Indians of this desert country know its secrets. Three thousand or more years ago they came here. They found mesas and mountains; they followed canyons where water wandered over the stones, and saw great natural caves high in the canyon walls.

[74]

ROAD-RUNNER

"Here is the end of our journey," they said among themselves. "We can plant our corn by the water in the canyon. We can dig shallow pits, and roof them over with bark from the cedars and pines, for houses. If enemies come, we can climb to those caves in the canyon walls and live there. From the yucca plants we can get fiber for weaving. The fruits of the cactus are good to eat, and the little pines have nuts in their cones. This is a good land."

Thus these first Indians settled in the desert. They wove such beautiful baskets that we now call them the "Basket Makers," though they have been dead and gone for centuries. They did not make pottery at first, but cooked in baskets which were so closely woven that they held water. Hot stones were dropped into them with wooden tongs to make the water boil. Later, these Indians found that by smearing the sides of a basket with wet clay they could make it last longer. Some of the baskets caught fire and burned away, leaving a rough clay pot, baked hard. After this the Basket Makers began to make crude pottery, and today we still find pieces of it with marks of the basket pressed on the outside. The baskets had beautiful designs woven into them in color. When pottery was made later, these Indians painted it in similar patterns.

This went on for centuries. Then other Indians came. These newcomers brought the knowledge of making better pottery. Their pots were thin, well made, and painted with wonderful colored designs.

Gradually the Indians left their pit-and-bark houses which were much like the earth lodge of Buffalo-Calf's people. They began to build square houses of poles and willow twigs woven together and plastered with the desert mud. Villages of these houses were scattered over the country, but always near water.

[75]

BASKET-MAKER
BARK HUT
FLOOR-PLAN

KIVA — THE
UNDERGROUND
CEREMONIAL
ROOM
FLOOR-PLAN

POLE-AND-ADOBE
(WATTLE-AND-MUD)
HOUSE BUILT ON
THE MESAS AFTER
THE BASKET-MAKERS..
FLOOR-PLAN

STONE-AND-ADOBE
HOUSE —
BUILT IN
CAVES AND
LATER ON
THE MESAS

HOUSES LIKE THIS
ARE SEEN IN
PRESENT-DAY
PUEBLOS-
FLOOR-PLAN

FLOOR-PLAN
PRESENT-DAY THATCHED
HOUSE OF APACHES IN ARIZONA

FLOOR-
PLAN
THE EARTH-LODGE OF
BUFFALO-CALF'S PEOPLE
ON THE PLAINS

FLOOR
PLAN
PRESENT-DAY HOGAN BUILT BY
THE NAVAHO — LOG-AND-EARTH-

It is a curious thing that in each village there was at least one room like the pit-and-bark houses used by the Basket Makers. The only difference was that these pits went farther down into the ground. Finally they became underground rooms entirely, round, deep and roofed over on top. To reach the bottom the visitor climbed down a log that had been notched to make a ladder. In the villages of the Desert Indians today, you can still see these round, underground rooms, called "kivas." That is, you can see the roofs and the tops of the ladders, but few white people have ever been inside, for this is the place where medicine men keep the tribal secrets. Here old men teach ceremonial lore to the young.

For hundreds of years these pole-and-adobe villages grew and prospered; then a wild, savage race of Indians from far away swooped down on them. They wandered down the canyons raiding the cornfields, killing the men, women and children. They stormed the villages and knocked them down. The village people that were left held off the invaders as best they could with their bows and spears. Then they scurried up into the old caves in the canyon walls, once used by the Basket Makers. Here they fought by hurling down stones and heavy rocks.

The invaders took what corn and other property they could carry, and went away from the villages. But they stayed in the Desert Country, wandering about, for they were hunters, following the deer. Today the descendants of these are the Navahos and Apaches. Navahos still live in pit-and-wood lodges called hogans. These are covered with earth like the old earth lodges of the Plains People. Apaches live in huts of brush without the mud covering. Both forms of houses are very much like the first shelters used by the Basket Makers.

The People who took to the cliffs continued to live in these caves. They learned to build stone walls, plastered with adobe, along the cave edge. Inside the larger caves, they built square houses, this time of stone instead of poles. They still had their kivas and their pottery

[76]

and basket-making ideas. They still planted their gardens and tended them during the day. But they came back at night to their caves, and a sharp-eyed lookout was always on duty to warn of danger.

PRESENT-DAY RUINS OF AN ANCIENT CITY OF THE CLIFF DWELLERS IN MESA VERDE NATIONAL PARK..

We call these ancient people the Cliff Dwellers. They, like the Basket Makers before them, have long been dead and gone, but their caves are still in the canyon walls, some in New Mexico, some in Arizona. In several of the large caves are still to be seen villages built of stone. The walls, watch towers and kivas are almost as they were left hundreds of years ago. We even find their pots beautifully painted, their blankets and robes. In the fire pits we find the bones of animals they ate, and kernels of corn and seeds. From all these things we are able to know something of the life of these strange people who lived in caves.

Little-Turtle was a boy who lived in those days. His family were Cliff Dwellers. His father, Coyote, and his uncle, Antelope, wore cotton loin cloths and woven fiber sandals. They had robes made of turkey feathers stripped from the quill and woven with yucca fiber. His mother, Painted-Bowl, wore a dress of tanned skins not unlike that worn by Buffalo-Calf's mother. Painted-Bowl wore sandals, too, and stockings knit from her own hair, which was cut when it grew long enough. The hair of the men was banged and bobbed.

[77]

MANNER OF MAKING A
TURKEY-FEATHER ROBE

The gardens of Little-Turtle's people were well cared for. They had learned a better way to grow corn, beans, squashes and peppers. In the old days their ancestors merely stuck the seeds into the ground near a river, and hoped for enough moisture and rain to grow them. Now irrigation was used. This was the watering of the fields by means of ditches fed by the river. Sometimes these ditches had to be dug for miles, to bring water from far away. In some parts of the desert such ditches were three or four feet deep. Indians plastered the ditches with clay, and built fires inside. This made the ditch bottoms as hard as the inside of a pot, and no water sank into the ground or was wasted. When the water came rolling down the big ditch to the fields, it separated into smaller ditches which ran all over the garden plots. It was like unbraiding a thick rope into little tangled strands. Thus the Indians were able to bring moisture to their soil whenever they needed it.

The Indians of today who live in these deserts use the same methods as Little-Turtle's people. Their gardens would not grow without the many miles of ditches. And some of these very ditches were dug by Little-Turtle's people, hundreds of years ago.

Painted-Bowl, Little-Turtle's mother, wove the most beautiful feather robes. She pulled the fuzzy part of the feather from the quill and wound it about yucca fiber strings. These strings she wove into soft light robes which were very warm. For a feather supply she kept wild turkeys in willow pens in part of the big cave. Baskets held her corn meal or flour. She ground the flour in a little open-topped box of plastered stones which held a large curved stone inside. On this she sprinkled kernels of corn and ground them by rubbing them with a smaller, flat stone. For bread, she mixed her meal with water, and she baked the bread on a hot stone griddle. It came off in round pieces like a very thin pancake. Desert Indians still make this bread. They call it "piki."

For her pottery Painted-Bowl rolled wet clay between her palms

until it looked like a short snake. She made the bottom of a pot by coiling several of these pieces round and round on a flat rock. As she worked she pinched the coils together, and finally smoothed them out to make a disc. Then, always coiling and pinching together, she built the sides of the pot of similar rolls of clay. First she made the pot swell outward; then she curved it in, until the opening was the size she wanted. When the coiling was finished she smoothed the sides with her fingers, which she kept dipping into water. Then she polished the whole pot with a smooth pebble. She dried and baked it a little in a fire, after which she decorated it with red, black and brown designs made from colored earths. Finally she baked it hard. Now it would hold water or beans or seeds and could be used for cooking.

One of the first things a girl had to learn was to carry water in such a pot on her head. She could not use her hands to hold it, because reaching the cave village was no easy matter. One climbed a hill from the river, then a series of notched logs. These were the Indian's ladders, and he never used the ones with two poles and cross pieces until after the white man came. After going up the ladders against the cliff, one finally stepped into footholds carved in the solid rock. Both hands were needed for the climbing and a very good balance. Water, food from the garden, even firewood was carried on the head up to the caves in this way.

Little-Turtle helped in the garden. His father and uncle were good hunters. They threw a curved stick, like a boomerang, at rabbits. Sometimes they threw short spears, and they shot antelope, deer and bear with the bow and arrow. In Little-Turtle's home there was always plenty of meat. But Cliff Dwellers depended on their gardens for most of their food. Game or no game, there was always a great quantity of corn and dried squash and beans stored away in the caves. There was always a hollow rock near the cave kept full of water, so when the wild raiders came, the Cliff Dwellers pulled up the log ladders and said "catch us if you can!"

[79]

Little-Turtle's village was divided into clans or groups. Each clan had its own totems. These were sacred animals whose spirits watched over the clan and brought health and luck. Children joined the clans of their mothers, not their fathers. Thus their uncles were more helpful in teaching them than their own fathers. Each clan had its kiva, where the boys were brought up by the old men in the mysteries and secrets of living a good life. Here they learned the dances and ceremonials for bringing rain, good hunting, and a plentiful harvest. During the year dances were performed, with beautifully painted masks and costumes, to the beating of drums and gourd rattles. The people were happy. The color of the desert entered into their lives.

These Indians learned to build their stone houses again in the valleys away from the caves. When the tribes grew stronger they built huge apartment buildings, sometimes in circles, with one story on top of another in broad steps. The outside of the building looked like a blank cliff, without windows. The warriors could fight from the roofs, as they did from the caves.

PART OF THE PUEBLO AT TAOS, NEW MEXICO WHERE INDIANS STILL LIVE AS THEY HAVE FOR CENTURIES...

These towns we now call pueblos, and some types of them can still be seen. The people live in them just about as they did in the old days, making baskets and bowls, weaving, and tending their gardens. Their costumes have changed but their dances are still as colorful as before.

[80]

He was glad that he would not have to meet people any more, going up and down. *See page 82.*

CHAPTER IX

LITTLE-TURTLE OF THE CLIFF DWELLERS

Little-Turtle was the most unhappy boy in all the world—or so he thought. From babyhood he had been clumsy. Of course his mother, Painted-Bowl, did not think so. She had given him his name because the symbol of the Turtle was sacred to her. She was certain that he would always arrive at the point where he was going. Others in the family were not so sure about the name, and shook their heads. A turtle was slow, and so was this boy. He had a thick shell and could not be taught. His father's sister had told him so; his own cousins had laughed at him. After being told these things many times, he began to believe them himself.

In the big house up there in the great cave, he felt himself of no use whatever. It all began when he was very little. His aunt had made a large pot. It was perfect in shape, and all the women and girls crowded about her when it was finished and admired it. How thin it was, and how light! And what beautiful bird designs, sweeping in such graceful curves!

Little-Turtle liked bright things. He pushed through the circle of girls, toddled toward the new pot, and tripped. His fall sent the pot crashing and it broke into a hundred pieces. He knew what had happened, but he couldn't run away.

His aunt picked him up and carried him to his mother, where she put him down suddenly on the cave floor. Though his mother took him into her arms, talking to the aunt, he couldn't help crying. The tears rolled down and smudged his face.

From that time on he was marked for misfortune. He tried to be careful, but there was always a loose stone or a corncob near him. He was always stepping on corncobs, usually with a bad result. As he grew older he grew more and more slow about his motions. He preferred to wait and think about what to do next and plan just how

to do it. In that way nothing wrong could happen. He would stand and think for so long that the children called him "that stupid Turtle," and he couldn't play their rapid games with them.

His mother was his playmate. She taught him things to do, and he worked them over and over so carefully that he learned them well. He could shred yucca leaves into good fiber for weaving, and he would sit by the hour stripping the fluff from the quills of turkey feathers. All the fluff from both sides came off in perfect corkscrew turns under his fingers.

Outside the houses, the sun struck the cave floor with friendly warmth; and on the canyon wall, across from the cave, it was always bringing out the bright reds and yellows of the rocks. It was always making new shadow patterns in the rock walls—butterflies, dance masks, bear forms. Little-Turtle liked to sit by his mother in the doorway and watch this gay world that the sun painted, away and down from the caves.

A real misfortune came to Little-Turtle when he was older. In climbing down from the cave, he fell and broke his leg. It did not heal well, and he always walked with a limp. After this happened, his Uncle Antelope made another set of steps in the rocks for him, and another set of ladders. This trail was longer than the old one but safer. He was glad that he would not have to meet people any more, going up and down. He was very grateful to his Uncle Antelope.

Painted-Bowl, his mother, taught him how to weed the corn and squash vines. Though he was slower than the other children, he did a better job. The weeds would not grow back again, once he went after their very roots, so his mother's corn patch grew better corn and better squashes than any of the other gardens. Of course, all this made the other children jealous.

"He thinks he's smart, just because his mother's corn is the best. But he isn't smart at all," they would grumble, bent over the green plants. They wanted to finish in a hurry to play Stump-The-Leader

[82]

up and down the cliff walls. But Little-Turtle did not look up. He just kept pulling weeds.

All this time the wise old men of his mother's clan were watching him. Some day he would join their secret ceremonies. What matter to them that he was slow? He worked well. No jeering or laughter made him hesitate, once he set out to do a thing.

"Mark my words," said old Turkey-Wing one day in the clan kiva, "that boy will do something big for our people some day. A ditch is not dug in a minute, and turtles grow slowly; but he will do something big."

"Yes," agreed the others who were squatting against the round wall. "Yes, perhaps. But he will not be a warrior. He will not be a great hunter. Men of that kind must have fast feet like the road-runner, arms that move as quickly as snakes, and a body tough and pliable as the puma. He is what his name is—a Turtle. But time will tell, time will tell."

CURVED RABBIT-STICK,
A BOOMERANG

When Uncle Antelope took Little-Turtle out on the mesa top, he opened the lad a new and wonderful world. He pointed out all the birds, beasts and reptiles, and named them. He told the child the old stories of Great Beings who live on the earth and in the sky, making the rivers run, bringing rain, keeping the sun bright and shining. He showed the boy how to throw the curved stick and the spear. Then he left Little-Turtle to himself, to think about all these strange things.

When Little-Turtle wandered in the desert by himself, he did not use the sticks-of-death. He did not care to kill the rabbits or see the antelope fall dead. Corn and beans and squashes were good enough for him to eat. Why should he kill these little brothers of the mesa? So Little-Turtle played by himself on the rim of the desert.

[83]

Out there beyond the mesa the earth seemed to catch the sky and pull it down like a blue blanket over a door. Below him the desert spread out, red as paint, broken by streaks of black and purple in the hills, yellow and brown in the mesa walls. It was his world, and here he lived, returning to the cliff houses only at night, and then by his private stairway.

He did not talk to the other children. He talked to his little animal friends instead. The magpie came at his call, flirting his long black tail. The bluejay and grouse ate cracked corn from his fingers. He could walk up to a prairie dog and chatter to him. The little fellows did not run into their burrows, but came out and sat upright during the conversation. He could gobble until the wild turkeys fed close to him among the pine needles as though he were another turkey. Thus he wandered about, making friends everywhere; and, in watching the movements of animals and birds, he gradually learned how to move quickly without stumbling.

In his journeys he discovered things that his people did not know. Following where a lizard led, he found a hole in the earth. He pushed a hollow reed down into the hole, placed his lips over the end and drew up water, clear and pure—better than river water. His people knew two trails up over the mesa. These made the journey many miles shorter than when they followed the canyon, from the cedar slopes back to the caves. But the rabbits showed Little-Turtle another trail even shorter, starting not far from his well. He had to make most of it himself, and it was a dangerous trail but he was not afraid. He took his time, and made it well, and then he always used it to cross the mesa.

First he climbed down a sort of gully; then he came to a cave-like opening. Down through this he dropped, just so, and landed—just so. By squirming down another gully, hanging to the bare cliff, he reached the desert floor below. It was hard work. He spent days at a time digging out each step in the rock and making it perfect.

There was one very bad place, however, where an overhanging, flat rock threatened to give way. One good push and it would go out and down, sending tons of rock into his gully. This would fill his canyon with stones, like a bowl filled with corn. At first when he went down or came up, he hardly dared breathe at this point. When he had done it twelve times without the rock falling, he began to think that he was not so clumsy as the children had said.

He often wondered what the outer world was like. Those great, golden deserts—what did they hold? To the east, men said, were plains, and mountains so high they plugged the sky as a corncob plugs a gourd. Beyond them, more plains with grass growing thick and tall, as far as the eye could see. Here the Black-Antelope-With-Hump, the buffalo, grazed by the thousands. That seemed unbelievable.

Out there in the desert to the northeast lived Enemy People. In the stories-of-long-ago that the wise men told in the kiva, he had learned how once these enemies had raided his people. They had killed many and looted the gardens. It was these enemies who had made his people leave their pole-and-stick houses on the mesas and go into the caves. But of course that had happened very long ago. The raiders had vanished into the red desert. Would they ever return again?

One day Little-Turtle saw a strange thing. Coming out of a canyon to the north was a man. As he looked another came, and another. They were so far away that they looked like black dots. Little-Turtle gazed so steadily that the Sun-Dancers made his eyes swim with tears, and those black dots went all wobbly. He rubbed his eyes, shaded them carefully, and looked again. The black dots were still coming, one at a time, out of the canyon.

"How odd," he thought. "Are they cave-people? Cave-people seldom move away unless the water gives out, and this has been a wet year. The crops are good everywhere. But here are many men."

Down on the desert floor, far off, a little brook wandered all by it-self among the hot rocks. Here old Blue-Corn had a garden patch, with corn and pumpkins. He used the last water from the brook before it sank out of sight in the desert sand. Blue-Corn was a lonely man, a hunter, and spent most of his time in the cedar hills. He tended his garden on his way to and from the hills.

Little-Turtle saw him now, just a tiny figure among his corn stalks. The old man was bent over, with his back to the line of marching men, and he did not see them. Then he straightened up. Had he now seen the men? Would Blue-Corn and the strangers talk? What would they say?

But Blue-Corn moved away from them. He started to run. The first man had a stick in his hand—was it a bow? Little-Turtle had a hard time making it all out, with the desert floor dancing in the heat waves. But Blue-Corn fell down suddenly among the dusty corn leaves. He did not get up. The men gathered in a group, talking, and making motions.

Then Little-Turtle understood. In some unbelievable way, Bad-People, Enemy-People, had come. They had killed Blue-Corn. What would happen now? This war-party would walk around the mesa, following the canyon, and would find the fields where men, women and children were scattered. These would be killed before they could climb to their caves. And Little-Turtle, up here on the mesa, could not run fast enough, with his bad foot, to give them warning!

Then Little-Turtle had an idea. He slipped down through that part of his trail that was like a cave. The walls of his secret canyon were so shaped that a yell or even a spoken word would echo back and forth a great many times. One voice would be heard down below, he thought, like a great many people talking. All the time he was climbing down he kept talking in a loud voice, until his own ears rumbled as though they were hearing many drums. Then he passed that overhanging ledge, very carefully, not talking, and came in sight of the men below. He pretended not to see them but talked back and forth as though there were many people behind him, and made motions and gestures to

[86]

those make-believe people. When he looked out of the corner of his eye, he saw that the band of men had divided into two parts. One band was running swiftly toward him. There must have been fifty warriors. One of them shot an arrow which Little-Turtle could not see, but which struck the roof of his cave and was shattered into many pieces.

Now he did another odd thing. He stood up on a rock and began yelling. He waved his arms toward all parts of his canyon as though warning his friends. Another arrow came and he hid behind a rock. The warriors had reached his trail. They began to climb the steps he had cut in the rocky wall. He made all the noises he knew how. The place fairly screeched with his yells, as though there were dozens of women and children behind there.

The warriors came on, climbing and puffing. Little-Turtle saw spears, round shields. He saw long hair parted in the middle, and eagle feathers bobbed up over the edges of rocks. He thought that he had never seen such cruel faces as lurched up from below, streaked and painted for war. There was no doubt about it now. These were men climbing to kill!

Little-Turtle felt sick at the pit of his stomach, but he remembered all that he had planned during that instant when Blue-Corn fell. Behind sheltering brush he crept upward again to that cave-like place with its overhanging rock. There he picked up a cedar staff that he had used in making the trail, and crawled above the rock. Very carefully he placed the pointed stick in a crack. His body doubled, his muscles tightened as he pried with all his might.

There was a piercing yell from below. The cliff leaned outward, seemed to come apart slowly. Then his ears were deaf from the noise of the world falling down. He clung desperately to his foothold. When he opened his eyes he saw that his gully was full of great rocks. Clouds of yellow dust smoked down the cliff and spread over the desert floor. When it lifted, he saw that the warriors of the second band were running away as fast as startled antelope.

Behind him over the mesa came men from his village. Their white cotton loin-cloths flapped in the sun, their hands bristled with bows and spears. But they need not fight now. Of all the fifty enemy warriors who had climbed Little-Turtle's canyon, not one was left. All that remained was a war-shield, face up in a bed of cactus. The clumsy boy had saved his people.

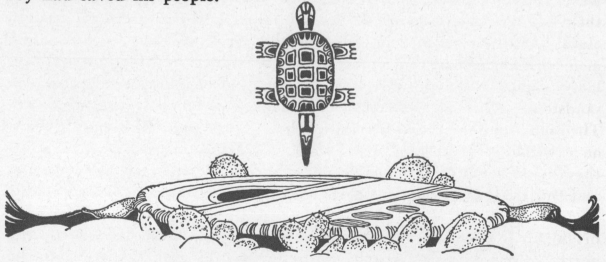

CHAPTER X
WHAT CORN-FLOWER FOUND

Corn-Flower lived hundreds of years after Little-Turtle. The Cliff Dwellers were already forgotten, and their great cave cities were deserted. Once before, after the days of the first Basket Makers, Indians had built towns on the mesa tops, but those towns had been houses of woven willows plastered with adobe.

The town where Corn-Flower lived was built on the mesa, but this time it had walls of stones, carefully laid. It was one huge apartment building, several stories high like a great pile of flat blocks laid one on another. Each story was smaller than the one below, so that the building looked something like a giant flight of steps leading up on all sides to a platform on top. Corn fields still spread their green squares along the river, and ditches wound through them like silver snakes. The trail from the town to the river was a staircase of many steps hewn in the rock.

It was a busy village, this place where Corn-Flower lived. Hunters climbed the stair trail with antelope and deer meat, women and girls were forever passing with water pots, corn baskets and firewood on their heads. In the rooms of the town quick fingers wove cotton into cloth. Turkeys gobbled in willow pens. From the nearby hills came men with chunks of blue stone, which we know as turquoise. These large stones were chipped into pieces by other men, and ground on sandstone. Out of the larger bits the jewelers made ear pendants. Through smaller chips they drilled holes, threaded these rough beads on rawhide strings and rubbed them down in sandstone grooves until they made smooth, rounded beads. The town was rich in turquoise, and this sky-blue stone was prized by all the people.

In Mexico, far to the south, there was no turquoise, but there were bright birds which were not to be found in the desert country of the north. Corn-Flower's people wanted these bright feathers and the

Mexicans wanted turquoise. So once in a while, sometimes years apart, traders from Mexico wandered into the deserts carrying on their backs bundles of feathers which they traded for turquoise. Thus brilliant parrot plumes and the skins of humming birds found their way into head dresses and dance masks of the desert people, while the traders, taking home the turquoise, were richly rewarded with gold in their own country.

From babyhood, Corn-Flower had heard these traders speak of white men. She had heard how a pale-faced man with a black beard named Cortez had come, bringing many other white men with him over an ocean, in great baskets with white wings. This was the Indians' description of ships with sails. Cortez and his men, the traders said, had conquered the Mexican Indians with long knives of metal-colored-like-water, which they called swords, and lightning-and-thunder sticks, which we know were the Spanish match-lock blunderbusses. The traders said, also, that these white men sat on great beasts, that galloped without fear, which they called horses.

In later years, other tales crept up from the towns in the southern deserts—stories of men in brown robes who carried crossed sticks in their hands and talked about an unseen god. By the time the stories reached the village of Corn-Flower, they were mixed and twisted, and most of the townspeople did not believe in them at all, but Corn-Flower never forgot these strange beings. She talked to her friends about them, and wondered whether they were as tall as a cedar tree, and whether the ground thundered when they walked. Lizard-Boy even took a bundle of black-dyed cotton and stuck it to his chin with pitch, to see what a beard might feel like. But all the children laughed. Surely no living person looked as funny as that!

When the days of Autumn came to the desert, and the brown corn stalks whispered dry talk in their leaves, harvest festivals began. Great drums boomed and rolled out their message to the Spirits of Earth and Sky.

[90]

"We give thanks to Thee, O Earth Mother, for our corn," they thundered.

"We are happy with heavy baskets of beans!

"We are glad, we are happy, our hearts beat gladness with the drums!"

Day after day came people from the kivas, gay with bright paint and masks, to dance in the open square before the town. There was never an end to the lilting chants, and the pad-pad of quick feet on the earth. Koshare, the Delight-Makers, pranced among the crowds, playing jokes, making the people laugh. And over all hung the sweet smell of cedar smoke and broiled venison.

The days of fall were nutting days. Bands of people left the town to camp in the hills. The mountains were gold with aspen trees. And here grew the pinon pines, short trees with stubby cones. In these cones crouched small nuts the size of a finger nail. They were bitter when eaten green, but when roasted contained sweet meats inside.

Corn-Flower went with a group of nut gatherers. There were women, children, warriors and a few old men. Beyond deep canyons the hills rose up, ridge on ridge like folds in a blanket. The pinon trees grew on the lower ranges, and here the people camped under the stars at night, and wandered from tree to tree during the day.

Corn-Flower was a good cone finder. She ran ahead of the others, sniffing the keen, cool air of Fall. She saw a clump of heavily loaded trees across a ravine and bounded down hill and toward it. But in the dry arroyo she halted, her heart thumping like a fast-beaten drum.

An animal stood there in the sun. It was larger than any she had ever seen. Its long neck hung down, and a river of hair fell from the ridge of it in ripples. Its tail was not that of a deer or an antelope, but

[91]

was like the long hair of many women tied together. And its hoofs were not in two pieces like deer hoofs, but heavy, round, and solid. She shrank into a clump of cedar. As she did so the wind changed so that it blew from her toward the animal, which looked in her direction. Its head came up with a jerk, its ears pointed upward, and it gave a long call like crazy laughter.

Corn-Flower was frightened. What was it? She saw that on its back was strapped an odd looking object, and it had straps on its head and face. From its mouth two long thongs hung to the ground. Surely this was an evil spirit! But it did not come after her. It merely gave that laughing call and then went back to hanging its head. In a few moments it seemed to be asleep.

Then another thing happened. Something that looked a little like a man stumbled up the arroyo. What kind of being was this that crept toward that spirit-thing? It crawled on hands and knees. It reached the spirit-animal and picked up the hanging thongs. The animal nuzzled it, and gave that laugh, and held up its head again, but the man (if it was a man) fell forward on his face and lay still.

Corn-Flower could remain there no longer. She raced back up the hill. Breathlessly she bounded in among the workers, gasping out her story. The women and children crowded together behind a rock, but the warriors grasped their bows and dropped from sight, creeping through the sage.

What was it all about? Corn-Flower told over and over what she had seen there in the arroyo. The women, children and old men could hardly wait for word until Meadow-Song, one of the warriors, returned to report.

"It is not a spirit," said he, but his eyes were large with wonder. "We do not know exactly, but we think that it is one of those things told about in the traders' tales—a White Man and his animal-for-carrying. But whether he is asleep we do not know. We wish the old men to come with us and investigate."

[92]

So, as cautiously and stealthily as pumas, the old men crept through the sage. Another wait. Corn-Flower could not hold her curiosity. She had seen these beings first, and they had not hurt her. What harm would there be if she went back and took just another peek from the top of the hill? She edged around the rock, unnoticed by the women, and scuttled like a grouse through the sage clumps.

Down below, the warriors were creeping up on the strange creatures. Then Dust-Cloud, one of the old men, walked forward slowly. The thing on the ground half rose, stretched out both arms, and pointed to his leg below the knee. The old man was looking at the leg now. Suddenly he straightened up and gave orders to the warriors, who all rushed in together.

This was too much for Corn-Flower. She slid down a clay bank and landed with a thump in the ravine. From rock to rock she sped, peering around, until she could hear the words the men were saying.

"It is a man, not a god. It is a white man. See, there at his neck —white like fresh rawhide! And he has that thing the traders call 'beard' on his face."

"He *is* a white man," proclaimed the old man, jerking upright from his investigation of the leg, "and he is ignorant of our Snake-Brothers' ways. One has bitten him, and he will die if we do not do something. I have great medicine against snake-bite. Go call Star-Woman to help me. Get water from the brook around those rocks. We will save the life of this white man."

It was not long before the whole band was grouped there in the arroyo, all talking at once.

"See, old Dust-Cloud is cutting away the cloth around the leg. But what has this stranger on his feet? Long tubes! And of leather!"

"And on the leather foot-tubes, there are bright things like stars of spikes. And on his chest a cloth that shines like sun-on-water!"

So they wondered about the boots and spurs and metal breast plate of the white man.

[93]

"The traders say that the thing on the animal is where he sits," said a young warrior, pointing to the saddle. "Surely that animal is not a terrible thing, it does not bound and try to trample the warriors around it."

"And now look—old Dust-Cloud is getting out his medicine, and binding the leg. He is the best person in our tribe for snake-bite. Why, I remember once—"

Thus the talk went on, while the old man worked. Corn-Flower stood as near as she dared. She saw the stranger's leg, black and swollen. His eyes were filled with pain. Little trickles of sweat poured down from his hair and crossed his dusty face like ditches across a cornfield. But he lay still and did not groan as Dust-Cloud worked. The animal (what did the traders call it? "Horse" was the word) merely stood still. Only his tail moved, switching from side to side. surely this was a miracle—a real, true white man and his horse in her desert country!

That afternoon the group camped in the arroyo. Dust-Cloud kept watch over the stranger who had fever and tossed about in the feather robes they gave him and mumbled words. Corn-Flower had never heard such strange words. They rippled on and on like water over stones, not like the soft gutteral words of her people.

"He is a human being," smiled Dust-Cloud, "and he is like us. Our medicines work on him, too. He was badly bitten by that Snake-Brother, but he will not die. Dust-Cloud's medicine is good."

After several days the stranger was able to sit up and look about him calmly. He smiled at Dust-Cloud and said words. He made signs. The result of it all was that, when the group of nut gatherers returned to the town on the mesa, they brought with them besides nuts, a real white man, riding a horse. And everyone stopped work for several days.

All that Fall the stranger lived in the town on the mesa. His room was next door to Corn-Flower's home, and it was she who took him

[94]

his meals of baked beans, chili, meat and bread. Dust-Cloud's medicine was making him well. Day after day he was learning Indian words from Corn-Flower and the men of the town, and they in turn were learning Spanish words. One of the first of these was his name for "town," which was "pueblo." That word is still used to denote an Indian village of those deserts. In a month he was talking Indian well enough to be understood. His name, he told them was Carlos, and his home was far away in a country called Spain.

With signs and his new-found words, the stranger told an astonishing tale. He had come into these deserts from Mexico with a band of Spaniards, under the leadership of one named Coronado, who sought gold. They had heard tales of seven cities of solid gold to be found to the north, but they had found that these stories were false. He himself was leader of a baggage train. He had gone on a scouting expedition, had become lost from his friends in the desert, and had been bitten by a rattlesnake while looking for the trail. He owed his life to having been found by Corn-Flower.

From the Indians he learned the trails to the eastern pueblos, where his friends had gone, and one day he rode away. But he promised to come back.

It was Corn-Flower who, several months later, sighted a dust cloud rolling along the desert with black specks moving beneath it. This was the baggage train Carlos had told about. As she watched, it turned toward the pueblo. Carlos himself was leading as it swung down the canyon, with other white men riding behind. Then came boxes rolling along on wooden discs like shields. Corn-Flower soon learned that these were wagons on wheels. The Indians had never seen wheels. They marveled at them, leaving long snake-tracks behind as they rolled. The huge boxes were covered with cloth stretched over hoops. Cattle pulled them, with horns long as spears, and they were followed by rabbit-eared deer and rabbit-eared horses. These strange animals, Carlos told Corn-Flower later, were oxen and burros and mules. The

[95]

train camped in the canyon, while its officers bargained for supplies of beans, corn-meal and peppers.

Carlos had already given Corn-Flower red cloth, beads of glass and a silver bracelet. Now, from the chicken coops in one wagon, he gave her three hens and a rooster. He presented her also with a burro, which he soon taught her to ride. All the other children from that time on were especially friendly with Corn-Flower.

When the wagons were loaded and the leader had said "goodby" to his friends at the pueblo, the baggage train pulled out of the canyon. The Indians were not to see white men again until Corn-Flower had grown to womanhood and had children of her own. When they came again, it was not to look for gold but to settle the country along the rivers. With them they brought other strange animals—sheep, goats and pigs.

Nowadays the Desert People weave blankets of wool clipped from descendants of those sheep and every pueblo has its burros and its chickens. This has gone on for so long a time, that the Indians themselves scarcely remember how those first chickens and that burro came to Corn-Flower in her desert pueblo.

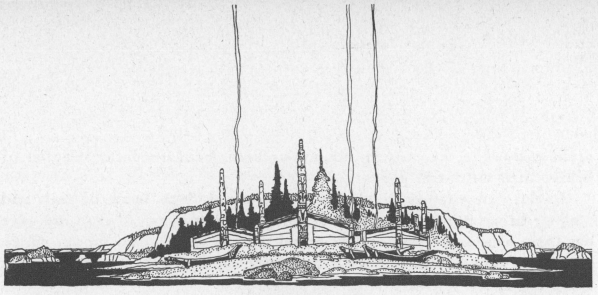

CHAPTER XI

PEOPLE OF THE RIVERS AND THE SEA

In the Northwest, where Canada meets the United States on the shore of the Pacific Ocean, live the People of the Rivers and the Sea. The boisterous ocean plays like a sea-lion. It swoops up and down the coasts in fast currents, nibbling at the shore. Here and there it has eaten away rocks, leaving deep bays and inlets. Mountains have fallen into the sea, making islands and leaving steep cliffs behind them. The tide climbs these cliffs every six hours, until the sea reaches a height of thirty feet in some places. Then it sinks again for another six hours. It is always restless, never still.

From high mountains inland, great rivers rush toward the sea. When the tide is going out, the rivers flow into the ocean. When the tide swoops in, the sea flows part way up the rivers. There is always a tug-of-war between them.

The creatures of the sea are endless in numbers. When the tide "flows" it brings clams. When it "ebbs" the clams burrow into the sands and mud. Mussels can be seen at the ebb-tide clinging thickly to wet rocks. Starfish, all colors and from the size of a butter-dish to that of a small dish pan, live on the mussels. They pry them steadily but slowly apart with their red and purple arms, as though they were opening a book. Round crabs scuttle in the pools left by the tide, wandering over the bottoms like fat spiders. There are to be found cuttle-fish, and the octopus with its big eyes and long tentacles.

Flounders and halibut lie on the sea bottom like flat stones, their two eyes on top. There are codfish and many other fish—too many to tell about. The little fishes are eaten by the big ones, and then the sea animals eat them.

HALIBUT AND HALIBUT HOOK

Among these animals are seals and sea-lions, which look like dogs with flippers instead of feet. There are porpoises and whales, which look like big fish, but are animals, just as cows are animals. The whale has lungs instead of gills to breathe with and would drown if he could not come to the surface every little while to breathe. When he comes up, he "spouts." That is, the breath comes out of a hole in the top of his head, blowing water with it. This spray shoots up exactly like a fountain. Often you can see a whale in the sea only by this fountain shooting against the sky.

Following the schools of fish, or sitting on the rocks waiting for one to come to the surface, are clouds of birds. There are terns, and gulls, and cormorants, while ravens walk along the beaches looking for tid-bits washed ashore.

This is the country of the salmon. You know salmon in cans. But where did this meat come from? The salmon begins as a tiny minnow hatched from an egg which was laid at the headwaters of a river, sometimes hundreds of miles from the sea. When the little salmon grows larger it swims downstream and into the ocean. It swims thousands of miles from the coast, and grows up in the sea. Finally it returns to the pool where it was born to lay its own eggs.

It is not so easy, this trip back up the river. Millions of other salmon come with it until the river boils with them. These fish fight their way up through fast currents, through foaming rapids. When they come to high falls, they leap into the air like silver torpedoes, trying to jump to a pool behind some rock where they can get a breath again. Then they go on. The weaker fish fall back and are washed away by the currents. Only the strongest salmon reach those quiet pools where they were hatched, and here the females lay their

QUINNAT SALMON (FEMALE)

THE MALE SALMON FIGHTS HIS RIVALS . . . . . DURING FOUR WEEKS OF SWIMMING UPSTREAM HIS JAWS GROW OUT AS SHOWN.

[98]

eggs. When that is done, the life work of the salmon is over. And now these salmon die, by the hundreds and the thousands. But the salmon in the can was caught long before it reached the quiet pools.

Although this dying by thousands seems hard on the salmon, it is good luck for other creatures. Bears—black, brown, and grizzly—flock to the river banks and eat until they can eat no more. Eagles by the hundreds wheel out of the skies to carry salmon to their rocks and crags. Thousands of ravens croak and caw, beating the air with satin-black wings. Foxes come, and wolves, skunks and mink. There is no end of feasting on this silver horde. But it doesn't matter. The eggs are laid and will hatch, and grow more millions of salmon for the next year, and next and forever.

In this country of tides and rushing currents and millions of fish, live Indians. They are different in many ways from the people of Little-Turtle, or Buffalo-Calf, or Otter-Tail. Their bodies are heavier, and the men grow sparse beards and mustaches, which few Indians do. In the old days, however, they pulled out all these hairs with two clam shells used like tweezers, thus keeping themselves beardless. The slant of their eyes makes their faces look quite like the Chinese. People think that their ancestors, as well as the ancestors of all other American Indians, came from Asia across Bering Strait to Alaska. But it was so long ago that no Indian remembers any story about it.

In the days before Columbus, these Indians were living very well. There was no end to food, on land or in the water. In this country they found "jadeite," a very hard, greenish stone, and this they made into tools that were much better than the flint or obsidian tools of the other Indians. The edges kept sharp for a long time and could be used for chisels and gouges and adzes to carve wood.

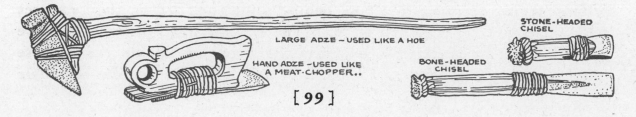

LARGE ADZE – USED LIKE A HOE

HAND ADZE – USED LIKE A MEAT-CHOPPER..

STONE-HEADED CHISEL

BONE-HEADED CHISEL

[99]

There was plenty of wood on which to use these tools, for great cedars and spruces and pines grew along the cliffs. There was such good material that these Indians did not use bark or skin or rocks for houses, but made them of planks split from the great cedars. To make the planks, they girdled a tree by hacking the bark away from the trunk all around, in a ring near the roots. This killed the tree in a year's time, and there were always trees being girdled for future lumber. The tree seasoned and dried out while it was standing. Often the Indians climbed up a live tree, to a point as far from the ground as the length they wanted their planks to be. Here they fixed a little platform against the trunk with ropes and boards.

Standing on the platform they chopped a huge notch on the side that would give the best planking. Placing wedges in a row in this cut, they drove them in with stone hammers until one great slab came away from the tree. Men below cut this loose with adzes and a fire built at the base, after which other slabs were wedged out and cut away. On the ground these huge beams were split into thinner planks. This splitting was deftly done. Whether from green timber or dead, seasoned stuff, the planks were of uniform thickness their entire length.

The planks were trimmed and finished with adzes until they were the right size. Some of them were two feet wide, twenty feet long, and an inch to three inches thick. When there were enough planks, a house was built.

The builders dug out a room underground and leveled it off, as we have seen in the earth lodge of Buffalo-Calf's people. In the center they dug a large rectangle below the floor and leveled this off, making a step down. Here was the sitting place for the people, about the fire which was sunk still lower in the center. When so much was finished, the builders set up heavy carved poles to make a frame. Then they drilled holes through the planks, and tied them to the frame with cedar bark thongs, or rawhide. The wall planks overlapped just as the planks on a clapboarded house do today, but the Indians'

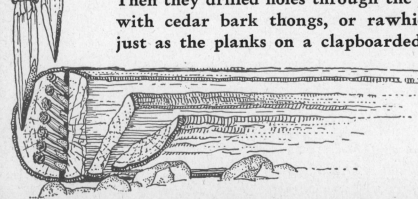

HAND HAMMER

WOODEN WEDGES

[100]

planks were so wide that it took only four or five to make a wall. The roof slanted with a gable end, as wooden houses now do. Inside, around the walls, a plank floor was laid, and plank walls divided the house into little rooms, all opening out toward the sitting place and the fire in the center. In each of these rooms lived a family.

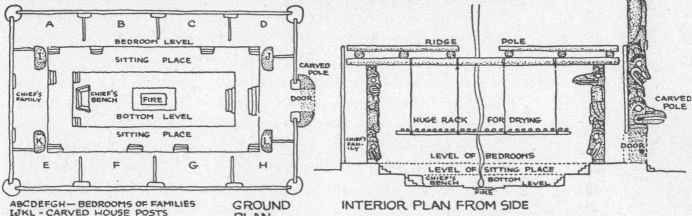

ABCDEFGH — BEDROOMS OF FAMILIES
IJKL - CARVED HOUSE POSTS

GROUND PLAN

INTERIOR PLAN FROM SIDE

Little-Raven lived in such a room. His mother was Sea-Spray, and his father Bear-Head. His father was a great warrior. He had led a war party in their canoes far to the north, where the tides ripped against the cliffs with the noise of thunder. And he had fought his enemies in his armor of sticks, with his carved bear's head helmet protecting him from the blows of whale-bone clubs. Those enemies had killed his own father years before, and Bear-Head was sworn to avenge his father's death. So he fought like the very bear which was his totem, and killed many enemies with his strong cedar bow and his elk antler club.

His canoe, coming home, had its gunwales lined with scalps of the enemy, and they flapped so hard in the stiff wind that they beat the sides of the canoe like many drumsticks. This was a lucky sign, and the men at the carved paddles dug into the salt waves with a will, and swung up the river and to the beach in front of the village. There was a great dance with carved masks and sticks and beautifully painted rattles to celebrate the event.

[101]

Bear-Head had not only taken many scalps and evened an old score. He had brought back several captives, who would now be slaves for his family. There were three women and a boy and a girl. These would carry the wood and the water and cook the food; and this would give Raven's mother a chance to spend all her time weaving her beautiful blankets of dyed mountain-goat's wool and plaiting her wonderful baskets. Bear-Head himself could now carve masks and helmets and totem poles and new canoes, without worrying about household duties.

The captives were sorrowful at first and grumbled. But this new village was really much better than their own. Besides, there were other captives, from their tribe, in neighboring houses, and when they had forgotten the noise of that awful battle, they settled down to enjoy themselves as best they could. At any rate, they would not have to work any harder than they had always worked.

Raven liked the boy and the girl his father had brought. The boy was Whale-Tooth, and the girl Cedar-Bough. He asked his father if he might have them for his own, and Bear-Head, after thinking about it for a time, gave them to him.

Though the boy sulked and the girl cried at first, they soon became fast friends with Raven. It was not at all like two slaves and a master. Raven was a friendly boy and the three children romped in the damp cedar forests and along the river and were always exploring the edges of the sea.

Cedar-Bough was rightly named. What she did not know about bark of the cedar tree could be swallowed by a minnow. She stripped bark from the yellow cedar, soaked it in salt water until it was exactly right, and then hackled it, or pounded it between two boards until it separated into strands as soft as dog-hair but wide as a fingernail. This she twined into cloaks for cold weather or made into baskets or fringed aprons for herself and Raven's sisters.

Whale-Tooth could make perfect fish traps out of willow twigs.

[102]

They were long baskets with wide wings on each side. A basket was laid in the center of a stream and anchored with rocks, and the wings were spread out on each side to the banks. Fish coming down the stream would strike the wing walls, swim along until they came to the basket, and go in. Pointed sticks guarded the basket mouth so they could not come out.

For meals, Raven's tribe had bear meat, deer, elk, rabbit, salmon, cod, halibut, smelts, seal and sea-lion, porpoise and whale. All of it was passed around in long bowls shaped like little canoes or carved in the forms of whales and seals. To every two people there was always a big bowl of seal fat or oil, for these People of the Sea liked plenty of fat. It kept them in good shape, gave plenty of warmth when they were working in the cold sea, and carried them through a winter very well. So most of the food, whether dried halibut toasted on a stick, or bear ham, was dipped into the grease-bowl before eating. After all, it was not so different from eating butter on bread.

Bear-Head decided to make a new sea-going canoe. He never tired of making things. Raven and Whale-Tooth helped. First a cedar, standing dead for two years and well seasoned, was cut down. Then Bear-Head took his biggest adze and went to work. He hoed that wood as a farmer today hoes corn, and the chips flew. After days of labor, Raven keeping the edges of the adzes ground sharp, the canoe took shape. It was long, and tapered to a flat tail behind and a long snout in front. Now the friends of Bear-Head helped him to cut out the inside with adzes. It took weeks, but finally there it was, all but the finishing. The tree had been several feet thick, but even a boat three feet wide at the gunwales or top edges couldn't stand the waves of the sea; they would come right in over. So the ticklish job of spreading those side walls of the canoe was at hand.

First the men filled it with water, close to the top. Then the old men came along. This was their particular work. They built great fires and heated piles of stones white hot. Raven and Whale-Tooth

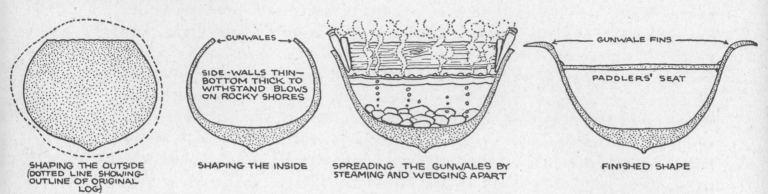

SHAPING THE OUTSIDE
(DOTTED LINE SHOWING
OUTLINE OF ORIGINAL
LOG)

SHAPING THE INSIDE

SPREADING THE GUNWALES BY
STEAMING AND WEDGING APART

FINISHED SHAPE

worked like beavers bringing new stones. Then the old men dropped the heated stones into the water in the canoe. The first stones made a loud sizzle and a zipping sound when they struck, and the old men ducked down beside the canoe, because the rocks exploded every which way on touching the cold water. But after awhile the water warmed up and, as pile after pile of stones zipped in, it boiled merrily. This was kept up for hours and hours, until the sides of the cedar canoe were wet through and steaming.

They were now pliable and big wedges of hewn plank were pounded into the inside with clubs. It was slow at first, but after awhile the side walls bulged outward. With more boiling and more wedges, they spread out and out, until finally the inside of the canoe, instead of measuring three feet from side to side, measured seven. The edges of the gunwales turned over and outward like long fins. Now, when a wave struck, it would follow up the sweeping sides of the canoe and the fins at the edge would turn it over as a plough turns earth. When the wide thwarts, or seats, had been driven in and lashed tight, the wedges were taken away. The water was dumped out, the stone piles removed from the bottom, and it was all ready for the carving.

Bear-Head marked out the totem symbols. There was his Bear totem at the tip of the long prow, with wide nostrils and big eyes, and the face of a man between the jaws—because it was a grizzly bear, a killer. If it had been merely a black bear, no face mask would have peered from the jaws. Then came a raven, whose flight was swift. Then an otter, who always caught his fish. And then a flicker, for good luck and a safe return. At the flat tail, a sea-lion sprawled in sweeping lines, so that the waves could never harm the stern. There was also a whale, which always comes to the surface after sinking. A few salmon symbols leaping on and on were put in for battling the currents. After all these symbols had been carved, the painting began. When it was completed the village gathered around and pronounced it the most beautiful sea-going boat in the tribe.

There was to be a whale hunt. Raven and Whale-Tooth wanted very much to go along, so Raven was a good boy for a week, and Whale-Tooth did everything exactly right to prepare for the asking. Men did not usually take boys on a whale hunt, but Bear-Head thought that it might be a good thing to teach them while they were young, so he finally gave his consent.

The boat was launched in a place where the rocks had been carefully taken away from the bottom in a long lane. Seven men and the two boys scrambled in; and, amid a tangle of harpoons and lances and knives and coils of rope, with all the village yelping and shouting from shore, the big canoe struck the waves. To the people watching, it went out of sight. But it rose up again, like a seagull, and paddles flashed in the sun. They were off!

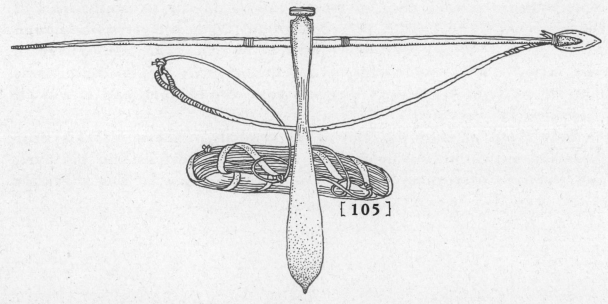

[105]

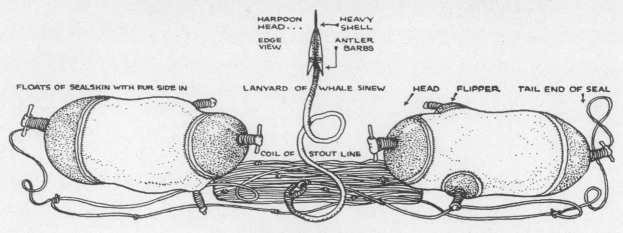

FLOATS OF SEALSKIN WITH FUR SIDE IN   LANYARD OF WHALE SINEW   HEAD   FLIPPER   TAIL END OF SEAL

HARPOON HEAD...   HEAVY SHELL   EDGE VIEW   ANTLER BARBS   COIL OF STOUT LINE

CHAPTER XII

RAVEN AND WHALE-TOOTH HUNT A WHALE

It was a beautiful morning when the big sea-canoe slid out of the river with the tide. The sky was bright blue, and the sun was warm, and white, fleecy clouds galloped along. All about lay the blue-black sea, romping in long rollers wearing helmets of foam.

Six men sat on the seats, three along each side. On one side were Cod-Fish, a husky warrior, and Sperm-Whale-Spouting, and Web-Foot, the best swimmer in the village. Ranged along the other side were Eagle-Goes-Up, who had deep scars on his face from many battles; Leaping Salmon, who had only one eye, the other having been lost in a fall down a cliff; and Crab-Runs-Sideways, a short man, but fat, who had more muscle in his great arms than one would think from looking at them.

These men lined the gunwales, and their brown bodies bent in perfect rhythm to a chant they sang, full from their throats. Eagle-Goes-Up had his head raised toward the sky, but he was not seeing clouds. He saw the great spirits of the sea and air that danced through the words of the chant. Crab-Runs-Sideways squinted at the bottom of the boat with no more expression than a clam. The rest gazed straight out to sea, and all the paddles dipped and cut through the water and flashed up and out and down again in perfect rhythm.

Bear-Head, Raven's father, stood at the stern with a long paddle.

It was a beautiful morning when the big sea-canoe slid out of the river with the tide.   *See page 106.*

He steered but made no movement except a twitch now and then in his arm muscles. He seemed as wooden as one of his own totem poles, but his eyes, shaded by heavy brows, swept the sea. Those eyes traveled along the black line where the sea ends and the sky creeps up from the foam, eyes beady as a bear's and as quick to see. His hair flowed back in a black mane. From his broad feet to his heavy-set jaw, he was a leader. The sun burnished his copper face.

Raven was proud of his father. From where he sat in the prow of the canoe, out of the wind, he could see all the men. "I shall be a warrior like Cod-Fish and Eagle-Goes-Up," he thought. "I shall have the strength of Crab-Runs-Sideways. But most of all, I will be a man among men, like Bear-Head." He lay among the coils of heavy rope. All about him were sealskin floats made of skins taken off whole and puffed up with air like odd-shaped balloons. On the bottom, carefully laid out, were the harpoons—long handles of yew, with sharp shell points set with bone barbs, resting in a socket at the end of the wood handle, and tied with whale sinew to the great rope. The sealskin floats were tied to the rope too. When a whale was harpooned the sharp shell head would go deep down and hold by the bone barbs, leaving the handle to float to the surface, tied by its own string to the great rope. Then the rope would be paid out, and the floats would go overboard and bob in the sea, slowing the whale down and tiring him out. At last the canoe, following the floats, would paddle alongside the whale, which would be killed by the long lances lying beside the harpoons. And that whale would soon after be meat for a feast.

The captive boy, Whale-Tooth, crouched between square plank water casks with plugged holes on top. The salt sea is no place for roaming without fresh drinking water. Spray from the waves hit the prow and came over everything in a fine mist. Whale-Tooth could put out his tongue and taste salt in the very air. At his feet were carved food boxes stored with meat and fish.

[107]

Hours passed, and Raven and Whale-Tooth were lulled by the swish of the sea running under the bottom. Distant islands looked to them like great sleeping bears. They passed porpoises flashing over and under the water in play, and a sea-lion who had killed a fish tossed it into the air to catch it again. Then Bear-Head gave a low call; the chant stopped; the paddles paused, and, following his pointing finger, the boys saw a fountain rising from the sea. Straight up it went, frayed out and blown over at the top. A whale!

The stern oar flicked at right angles in the hands of Bear-Head, and the paddles dipped again. The canoe turned in its course and sped toward the spouting whale. Now it stopped. A few minutes later that spray rose again, this time higher, for they were nearer to the whale. And now Raven could plainly see the great beast rolling in the valleys of the waves. My, but he was a big one! His back arched to the huge head in a black curve, which turned blinding white when the sun struck it. Nearer and nearer moved the canoe and larger and larger grew the whale.

Now Bear-Head gave his oar to Crab-Runs-Sideways and crept forward, sliding over the flat seats. Raven clambered back to sit with Whale-Tooth, under the center of the first thwart, between the water boxes.

Bear-Head carefully took up a harpoon. He tested the shell tip with his thumb and wiggled it cautiously in its socket, but he was gazing all the while at the whale. He felt of the ropes, and the skin floats, passing his hands over each in turn as though groping in the dark, but he knew that everything was ready.

The boat crept on. The whale was endwise to it, the great flukes, or tail, toward the bow. Every now and again the flukes rose and smacked the water gently, and Raven could see them when the canoe went downhill on a wave. Now Bear-Head crouched in the bow, poised like a puma about to spring. His right arm went up and back in a slow curve, and then his shoulders shot forward. His arm lunged and the harpoon bolted out like an arrow from a bow.

It happened in the wink of an eye, but Raven saw it all, and the pictures remained with him until he was an old man—that forward lunge, the harpoon in the air with the sun on its point, the thin sinew line trailing behind like a tail. And then a dull "chuck" as it stuck, and Bear-Head's body bent over, his hands gripping the prow of the canoe as he watched with those beady eyes.

Then things happened. Paddles struck the seats and slid to the bottom. Cod-Fish and Sperm-Whale-Spouting leaped past Raven's knee and dove for the floats. The heavy rope was being paid out frantically by Bear-Head, the coils whipping from his hands like great corkscrews. One skin float went over the side, then another, and another, and faster and faster went the rope coils until only one float was left and a few more coils of rope.

Raven stood up in the excitement. The canoe went downhill. The whale stood on his head, those great flukes against the sky like an odd tree, dripping. He was going straight down—sounding—not running away. He would go to the bottom! Now he had gone, and one by one the floats bobbed down behind him like great stones sinking. Then Cod-Fish struck Raven with his elbow, and the boy went

[109]

sprawling. He felt a tug on his ankle as a coil of the rope whipped around it. The canoe went out from under him, he was in the air, and the horrified faces of the men passed away from him in a blur.

Instinctively he took a deep gulp of breath, and then he was fighting, fighting water that shot past him in green bubbles. Down, down he went. His legs kicked. The water grew colder and colder, his ears were ringing, his head ached from the pressure. Then something struck him in the face and he grabbed it and held on. The tug went away from his leg, and he knew he was free. Would his breath hold out? What was this thing he held in his arms? Then he was above water again, gasping. But he was not hurt, and he was hugging the last sealskin float, which had pulled away from the line and set him free. He held on and went bobbing up and down over the waves.

And now the great carved prow of the canoe loomed over him. He could see the painted designs on the sides. Strong brown arms reached down and hauled him over the gunwale. Bear-Head was looking at him with jaw set, and Whale-Tooth's mouth hung open. Then Raven laughed, it seemed so funny to him, this being taken for a ride by a whale! And soon all the men wore smiles.

"Your medicine is good, Raven my son," Bear-Head said gently. "There are not many men, living or dead, who have ridden the depths with a whale and come back again to tell about it. At first I didn't want you to come on this hunt, but now I see that you have a great and good spirit hovering over you, The Raven. You will someday be a great whale-killer. And now, we will go and get that whale!"

But it was not so easy as that. The whale had gone to the bottom of the sea. He was trying to throw off his enemies who had struck him with that harpoon. He was somewhere below, deep down. The men in the canoe had no idea where he might come up. They could only wait.

Then, far off toward the island, something bobbed on the waves. A skin float! Another popped up near it, and another. The whale was coming up to spout! Bear-Head took the stern again, and the canoe began to move toward the floats. When the whale came up, spouting that fountain of his, the men bent to a fast chant, and the paddles fairly flew.

Then the whale ran away. That is, he began swimming toward the farthest island, toward the open sea beyond. The floats skimmed through the waves, wagging from side to side on the long line. Raven and Whale-Tooth, peering over the sides, could see them skip and jump from the top of one wave to another. Sometimes they went completely under, dragged down by that swimming monster. This was what was wanted. The more they dragged below the surface, the more they hindered the movements of the whale, and slowed him down.

The men did not chant now, merely paddled fast enough to keep those floats in sight. Now the whale paused to spout a little, and to wallow and thrash in the waves. But he could not get rid of the line. Then he raced on again.

Hours went by. The whale circled back again toward an island and slowed up. Bear-Head gave an order, and the canoe closed in. Perhaps the animal was tired enough now. Perhaps they could ride in and kill him. When they came alongside, Bear-Head and Eagle-Goes-Up each took a long lance. They poised on the bow, and when the canoe sidled in, almost touching the whale Bear-Head leaped first and Eagle-Goes-Up went after. They landed on the great back and stabbed with the lances as hard as they could, at just the right spot.

[111]

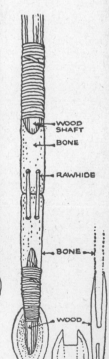

WHALE LANCE

WOOD SHAFT

BONE

RAWHIDE

BONE

WOOD

SHELL HEAD

The whale rolled over and the two men slid into the sea, hanging on to the poles of their lances. The men in the canoe were pushing their craft swiftly away from the great body, but they were not swift enough. Raven saw that the whale, in turning, had slid his tail under the canoe, and it was coming up, the flukes green in the sea water. There was a mighty heave, and the canoe and everything in it went into the air. Again Raven was in the sea, bobbing about. He swam and caught hold of a paddle. The water was churning, bubbling, gushing. The canoe was floating upside down, and all about were heads bobbing where the men swam toward it.

Then the lashing of that giant tail was over, and the water quieted down, and Bear-Head and Eagle-Goes-Up were on the great back again, waving their arms and yelling orders. The animal was dead. Now the men swam toward the whale, after fastening a line to the canoe, while Raven and Whale-Tooth followed. Eagle-Goes-Up helped the boys to the whale's back, and the men crawled up, climbing by the harpoon rope that was wound round the animal many times and tangled by his churning in the sea.

It did not take long to haul the canoe beside the whale, and with all men working they finally turned it right side up, draining out the water. The water casks were still safe, tied by cedar ropes to the seats, but paddles, lances and harpoons were floating all about. So were the little boxes of food—smoked meat and dried fish. However,

Web-Foot the swimmer went about gathering these things and tying them to a line fastened about his waist. When the last paddle and food box had been recovered, the men hauled him back to the whale.

This whale was the largest that Bear-Head had ever harpooned. It would take more than seven men and two boys to tow him to shore behind one canoe, for the shore was far off, a mere line on the horizon. But Bear-Head knew what to do.

All of them climbed aboard the canoe again, and paddled for the nearest island. Raven meanwhile washed the soaked meat and fish with fresh water from the wooden casks. As it dried again in the sun everybody ate, for with all this work they were very hungry. When they came close to shore, they found a flat sandy beach behind a group of projecting rocks, and here they landed, beaching the canoe. The seven men easily ran it up into the soft sand and propped it up with blocks of driftwood, so it would not topple over and break the gunwales.

Bear-Head took his firesticks, still dry because they had been wrapped in a sack made of seal membrane, and climbed up to the highest part of the rugged island. Raven and Whale-Tooth went along, picking up bits of dry wood as they climbed. Gulls and other sea birds wheeled about them, making shrill noises. They could look down the rock edges to where the sea pounded in thick, white surf.

Bear-Head quickly made a fire, and they all heaped on branches. When it was going well, the boys brought armfuls of damp ferns from the forest, and with these smothered the fire—not enough to put it out, but just enough to make great clouds of thick, billowing smoke. Then Bear-Head and Leaping-Salmon, who had climbed up with an elk skin, began to signal. They held the rawhide down in a sort of pouch over the fire until it was filled with smoke. Then, suddenly lifting the skin they let the smoke float skyward with a great puff that broadened out into a cloud. The length of time between puffs and the size of the puffs made the different signals.

[113]

Far away, on the mainland near the village, where a lookout always scanned the ocean, the little puffs were seen in the sky; and before dark, Raven could see tiny specks out on the sea—more canoes coming with help.

The new canoes arrived in the moonlight, and all of them went out to sea again. It was not hard to locate the dead whale, for Bear-Head had left the lances sticking in the great back, and had tied a robe to them to serve as a pennant. With many hands working they soon unwound the big rope and tied other ropes to the back, head and flippers. Ten canoes lined up on these ropes, and with all paddles churning the calm sea to a froth, the great hulk was slowly towed toward the sand beach.

Here they began cutting up the meat. Time meant everything for gulls would be down in swarms in the morning, and already crabs and fishes had found the kill and begun feeding. But by the next afternoon all that was good to eat on that whale had been made into meat, certain bones and teeth had been kept to be made into new tools, and the canoes started back on the home journey, leaving the gulls to come down and have a great feast on what was left.

There never had been such a feast as was held in the village along the river! The new canoe had been lucky. Everyone in it had been lucky, especially Raven. The whale steak and the whale oil went about freely, and they all ate until they could hold no more.

CHAPTER XIII

CEDAR-BOUGH'S BARGAIN

Cedar-Bough tried to be happy, but she could not. She would sit on a rock by the river as the copper-colored sun moved through the spruce trees and the totem poles threw black arms against the red sky. To the north were her people. When the Great Ladle was hung in the heavens and the Pole Star gleamed, she sang a little song:

"It is far to the glaciers, it is far to the Land of the Snows;

Farther than a fox can cry; farther than a wolf can howl;

O, Spirits of my People, O, Sacred Totems, take me home!"

One evening Raven heard her song. He did not know the words, but Cedar-Bough's voice was sad. He knew well what she thought about, and he went to his father, Bear-Head.

"Captives are never watched," he said. "Why could they not escape?"

"They could," said Bear-Head, "but they wouldn't. Many tribes are between our people and the people of Cedar-Bough, if you're thinking about her. Warriors of other tribes find escaped slaves, and they are slaves all over again—though worse treated in other places then here."

"But Cedar-Bough is sad," said Raven. "Couldn't something be done?"

Bear-Head said that nothing could be done, and another day, when Raven spoke again, his father looked grave.

"My son," he said, "some day you will be a warrior. You were not alive when this girl's people raided my village. I was but a lad, but I remember the women screaming and running for the forest. I remember the carved helmets of the painted warriors coming over the rocks. I can still hear the ring of blows, as clubs came down crushing bone. My father fell before he could reach for his bow. I ran to the cliff and hid, in a thick bush overlooking the sea. I saw their canoes going out of the river in the dusk, and there were dark patches hanging along the gunwales. Those were scalps, my boy, and one of them was my father's—your grandfather's. I vowed then that I would take scalp for scalp when I was a man; and when, returning home, I saw the blazing village making the woods red, I was bitter. Nothing can change all that. It is kill or be killed. I have taken scalp for scalp. I have taken captives. It has always been thus, and there will never be a change. You will understand, when you are a man. War is war."

But this talk did not satisfy Raven. What was the use? War was war. All Indians knew that. He would be a brave warrior, and fight with a helmet on, a carved raven's head with the beak over his eyes. But why should he fight Cedar-Bough's people? He had never seen them in their own land. True, they had raided his father's village and had taken scalps. Then Bear-Head had raided their villages in turn, and had taken scalps. To Raven the score was even, and if it was even, the game was over. But these thoughts were all confused in his head, and there was no use being sad. He'd go fishing with Whale-Tooth.

As they were fishing along the river, a canoe came up-stream. In it was Raven's mother. The three captive women and Cedar-Bough were paddling. The boys waved to them as they passed.

"Where are you going?" called Raven.

"After berries in the hills," called back his mother. "Take the

salmon home when you have finished, and your aunt, Crooked-Walk, will cook them. We will not be home tonight and may be gone for three days."

The women paddled in silence. When they came to a meadow where marsh grass was growing, they turned into a smaller stream which wound among rushes and then flowed into the forest. Where the hills came down through the trees, they pulled their canoe to the bank. Here was a shelter made of poles and a plank roof.

They took out the berry baskets, nested together, and Sea-Spray gave her orders. She would remain at the camp while the three women and Cedar-Bough went berrying. They would bring the baskets of berries back to the shack and would stay there over night. Meanwhile, Sea-Spray would not be idle. She would spin mountain goats' wool mixed with the woolly hair of white dogs.

The women and the girl divided the hills among them. Cedar-Bough being a young girl, should not go straight into the hills and underbrush as the others would do, because she might get lost. She was to follow a bubbling brook, never getting out of hearing of its song. Thus she could find her way back in the afternoon.

So Cedar-Bough strapped her big basket to her back, and went up the rocks, clutching her smaller hand basket. She was soon out of sight of the hut and of the other women. The brook came tumbling and roaring, and the sun shone on the white flecks of foam. Sometimes she walked in the moss along the banks, and sometimes across open places, partly covered with willow scrub and poplars and all kinds of tangled underbrush. Here and there were patches of blueberries growing close to the earth on dwarf bushes. They were thick and some were as large as her thumb nail. All she had to do was to place her small basket under the spray of berries and carefully pull them off. They bobbed and bounced, several at a time dropping down. When the hand basket was full she emptied it over her shoulder into the larger one.

Walking from the brook to a blueberry patch and back again to the brook was easier than going through the tangled underbrush between the patches. Now she realized why it was that women captives among these People of the Sea seldom tried to run away. The forest was no place for traveling. Spiked trees barred her at every turn, and the sharp granite rock cut her feet. But back along the brook were smooth-worn pebbles, cool and easy to walk on. So she waded up stream, climbing over the slippery places, always on the lookout for berries.

At one place where she stopped to rest, the brook had cut into the bank and a gravel bar extended around the bend. Great glaciers had ground the rocks into small pebbles and sand thousands of years ago, and had piled the gravel in hills. It was on one of these hills that she was resting.

Cedar-Bough had clay all over her feet so she went to wash them in the pool at the base of a large rock. She found a sharp stone to scrape the clay from her legs, and struck the stone against the big rock to clean it after each scraping. She turned her face toward the rock to get out of a cloud of mosquitoes, and then she noticed that the rock was black; it looked different from the other rocks she had been climbing all afternoon, and where her stone had struck it many times, it was another color. Hastily she began scraping at that place. The black came away, and left a reddish glow where she had scraped. Her big rock was solid copper! It had been dislodged by the great glacier in the long ago, and had been rolled and pounded and hammered along with gravel to this place.

Solid copper! She hardly knew what to do. If there was anything which these People of the Rivers and Sea valued above everything else, it was copper. The more a man had, the greater his place in the tribe. Not only could it be hammered easily into double-bladed fighting knives and arrow points and tools of all kinds, but any copper left over in a family was made into a special kind of thin shield, which was hung up

[118]

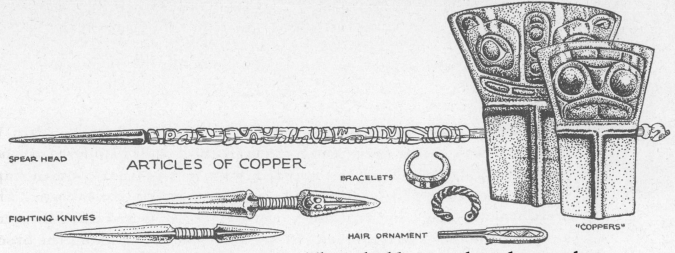

SPEAR HEAD

ARTICLES OF COPPER

BRACELETS

FIGHTING KNIVES

HAIR ORNAMENT

"COPPERS"

to show how rich its owners were. These shields were shaped somewhat like the axes you see nowadays, and were in size from a foot to three feet across. The owner of a three-foot "copper" was looked upon by his neighbors, as the owner of three very fine cars is looked upon today. And what Cedar-Bough had found was more than any man among these people had ever owned at one time.

She began scrambling about the big rock. Surely it would take five men to lift it! She looked all about on the gravel bar and, sure enough, there was more. She found a piece as big as her fist, and two nuggets the size of arrowheads. That was enough. Carefully she placed the small pieces under a carpet of moss, and spread clay over the scratches she had made on the large piece. Then she rushed through the hills picking berries. When she had enough for Sea-Spray's satisfaction, she went back to the shack.

All the other women had returned. Each was loaded with berries. It was a good year, and everybody was happy, but even Sea-Spray remarked how light hearted Cedar-Bough was. She sang snatches of song as she unrolled the sleeping mats and the robes. But she did not tell her secret to anyone.

That night as the Pole Star blazed in the sky, she sang a chant by the brook where the others could not hear.

"Oh, Spirits of my People! Hear me! I have found a way. Make my medicine strong. Give me strength and courage to carry out my plan!"

The berries were so thick, that by the next noon the women had as many as their canoe could carry. Cedar-Bough had gone back up her brook and had found other patches she had overlooked the day before. Also she had found three more small copper nuggets. These she hid in a bark roll beneath her apron.

The berries were put aboard the canoe, Sea-Spray gave her orders, and they went back downstream.

That evening in the big house, while the men sat about the fire, Cedar-Bough called Raven to her.

"Raven," she said, "your father gave me to you, along with Whale-Tooth. But you know and I know that I am really the property of Bear-Head. Do you think he would let us go—the three women and Whale-Tooth and myself?"

"It's no use," sadly replied Raven. "Bear-Head has said that he will not part with any captive owned in his family."

"But if I *bought* our freedom—with this?" and she held out her hand.

"Copper!" exclaimed Raven. "Where——"

"Never mind where," said Cedar-Bough. "You just come with me."

Rising, she walked among the men in the fire-square, right up to Bear-Head, and stood in front of him.

"Honorable Bear-Head," she began in a high voice, trying to be brave, "all the tribe knows you are a great warrior. You have taken

many scalps and burned many villages, and you took five captives from my own people."

"What—— who——" began Bear-Head, for slaves seldom spoke to an owner like this. "Well, what about it?" he growled, but not unkindly. He liked the spirit of this little girl.

"I have come to buy the freedom of your five captives!" said Cedar-Bough.

Bear-Head's eyes crinkled at the corners. "Just how are you going to buy the freedom of five very good slaves that I, Bear-Head, took with my own hand?" he asked.

By this time the people from the various rooms were crowding about, and all the men were smiling. Spunky little girl! Would Bear-Head punish her? She saw all these people. They did not look hostile, but friendly, and by a post stood the wondering Raven, with his arms folded. She went on:

"I have found copper. I have found enough copper so that you and your family will be the wealthiest people in all the tribes along this coast. You will never find it unless I show you where it is. You can kill me, you can burn me tied to a post, but I will never, never tell unless you promise us our freedom. And if you do not believe that I know where the copper is, look at this!"

Cedar-Bough had polished her copper bits until they shone. Now she dropped them with a wave of her hand on Bear-Head's sitting robe. They lay there so that all could see them shimmering in the light of the fire, like little pieces of the setting sun. Gasps of astonishment went around the circle, and Bear-Head lifted the pieces in his hand. Even here was enough for many arrows and knives.

"You have brought this copper," said Bear-Head, leaning forward. "It is good copper. How large is the piece you have found?"

Cedar-Bough's eyes never faltered. They gazed back into the beady eyes of the chief, and the blood of chiefs tingled in her veins. It was now or never, and she felt that her medicine was strong.

"I have found a solid piece," she began. "It might be as big as this bowl. That is to set me free. It might be as big as these two bowls. That is to set the boy, Whale-Tooth, free. It might be as big as the carved chest in your house-room. That is to set the three women free. I say, honorable Bear-Head, that the piece I found *might* be as big as your carved chest!"

Here the people crowded in, silent as a group of fish. There was a gasp here and there as women caught their breath, and there were no smiles on the faces of any of the men. If this little slave had found so much copper—it was not so—it just couldn't be.

"If that is true, I might listen to what you have to say," said Bear-Head. "But if it isn't—watch out. Bear-Head is a hard man, as you know. He is a warrior. He knows what to do with slaves that talk with two tongues. But if, as you say, you have found copper as large as my carved chest——"

"I said it *might* be as big as that," replied Cedar-Bough, "but it really isn't. It's *bigger*! It's as big as the great chest that Sea-Spray keeps her blankets in! And not only is it to set us *all five* free but you, yourself, will take us in your war canoe back to the land of my people, where we can find them again! It's true! All true! And you can beat me, torture me, kill me—I am your slave and only a little girl! But you will never, never find that copper without me! My medicine is strong! My father was a great man! And—— and——" but she had slumped to the floor, and she hugged her knees to keep back the sobs.

The people saw that she had spoken truly. And now Bear-Head had arisen from his robe, and picked up Cedar-Bough.

"Little Cedar-Bough," he said, "no one man has ever owned as much copper as that. If your tale is true, and not just something which you have imagined, I will do all that you have asked. I will set you free—and Whale-Tooth and the three women. I will bargain for the freedom of all the ten people who were captured from your villages, for I know that the owners of these will sell, for copper. And I, with

Raven, my son, will take you back to your own land, in my own canoe!"

That is how it came about that one day, soon after, a group of war canoes put out to sea with the tide. It was the first time these coasts had seen such a sight. These canoes would not return with black scalps fluttering in the wind along the gunwales. No captives would return in them, and there would be no charred ruins of totem poles and houses left behind.

In the first canoe stood a man with a helmet carved like the head of a bear. In the same canoe Raven was talking to Whale-Tooth and Cedar-Bough.

"Now, see here," Raven was saying, "I will grow up to be a warrior. And you, Whale-Tooth, will be a warrior. But when we grow up, let us remember those days when we were children. Let us remember how we went whale hunting. And how we all shredded cedar bark, and fished for salmon, and worked and played together. Our fathers say that 'war is war,' and that the only end for brave people is to die fighting. That may be so. But between your people and my people, let us never raid along the sea. Cedar-Bough drove her bargain, and I want to drive mine. Will you promise?" Whale-Tooth solemnly promised. And, when these children grew up, there was peace along these coasts for many, many years.

GLOSSARY

The pronunciations are given in parentheses.

adobe (a-dough′bee).   Desert clay mixed with water, combined with dried grass or straw and baked in the sun.

Apache (A-pah′chee).   A tribe of southwestern American Indians.

apakwa (a-pak′wah).   A strip of house covering made by sewing squares of birch-bark together.

arroyo (ăr-rŏy′o).   The gully in which a small stream runs, or the dry bed of such a stream.

buffalo (buff′a-low).   As used in this book, the word is the frontier name for bison. In reality, "buffalo" are natives of Africa and Asia, and are quite different from the American bison.

buffalo birds.   Small birds of the starling family which perch on the backs of the buffalo to eat the insects that hide in the thick fur of the animals.   These little birds often warn the buffalo of danger by alarmed chirpings, or by flying away.

butte (būte).   A hill or small mountain standing alone on a plain, especially one with steep sides.

coulee (koo′lee).   A deep ravine with sides that slope gently.

deadfall.   A trap made so that a log falls upon an animal and kills it.

ebb.   To flow backward—said of the tide when it is flowing back toward the ocean.

flow.   To move smoothly or continuously, as in the case of a liquid.   When the word is used in connection with the tide it means that the tide is moving toward the shore.

gully.   A small valley with steep sides.

gunwale (gun′wāl or gun′nel).   The upper edge of a boat's side.

irrigation (ear′ri-gā′shun).   Supplying water to dry land by digging ditches from a river or reservoir.

Koshare (kō-shar′ee).   The Delight-Makers who amused the Indians much as the circus clowns amuse us.

medicine (med′i-sin).   As used by the Indians this word meant not only something to be taken for sickness, but some power or charm that controlled or supplied magic strength or wisdom.

[**124**]

mesa (may'sa). A plateau, or flat-topped hill, with steeply sloping sides. Mesas are often found on the edges of deep valleys, which make one side of the mesa longer than the other.

Navaho (Nah'vah-hō). (Sometimes spelled Navajo but pronounced as though spelled with an "h" because in Spanish "j" is given the sound we give "h.") A tribe of American Indians now noted for their work as silversmiths and for the beautiful blankets woven by the women. Both silverwork and wool weaving were taught them by the Spaniards.

parfleche (par-flesh'). A piece of rawhide used for wrapping food or other supplies.

pemmican (pem'mi-kan). A very nourishing food made of dried buffalo (beef now used) pounded to a paste and mixed with fat. Usually dried fruit is added.

piki (pee'kee). A thin disc of bread made of corn flour and water and baked on a hot stone.

piñon (pin-yōne'). The Spanish word for seed, thus the piñon pine with cones which have edible seeds.

portage (pōr'taj). A place between two bodies of water where a canoe or other light boat is carried overland.

pueblo (pweb'low). This is the Spanish word for village. It is used to refer to the settlements of desert Indians in which a whole village lived in one great building.

ravine (rav-veen'). A channel worn in the earth's surface by running water.

stockade (stŏck-āde'). A line of strong posts set in the earth close together as a defense against the attack of enemies.

tomahawk (tŏm'a-hawk). A small ax used by Indians as a weapon of warfare or for hunting. Before the coming of the white men the heads were made of hard stone. Later the Indians traded for steel-headed tomahawks from the white men.

totem (tō'tĕm). The supposed spirit of something in nature (usually an animal or bird) which protects and guides a person or clan, and is thus venerated. Also an image of such subject.

travois (tra"vwah). A V-shaped carrier made of two poles with a platform or net between to carry baggage. Where the poles joined they were attached to a dog or horse. The other ends dragged on the ground.

wickiup (wick'ee-up). A hut made of a pole frame covered with reed mats, brushwood or bark.

yucca (yuck'ka). A plant with long, lancelike leaves from which a stem springs, bearing a mass of white blossoms at the top.

[125]

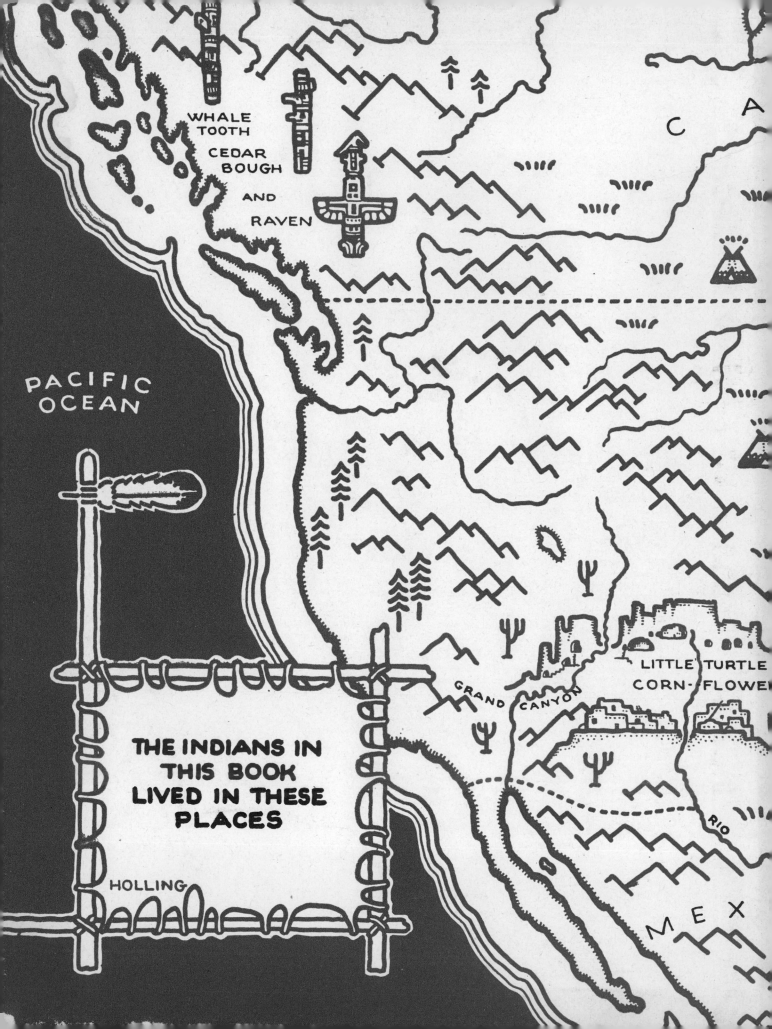

WHALE
TOOTH

CEDAR
BOUGH

AND

RAVEN

C A

PACIFIC
OCEAN

GRAND CANYON

LITTLE TURTLE
CORN-FLOWER

THE INDIANS IN
THIS BOOK
LIVED IN THESE
PLACES

RIO

HOLLING

M E X